Book Two

principle

SCIENCE

Activity-Centered Program
Teacher's Guide

Lucy Daniel
Rutherfordton-Spindale High School
Rutherfordton, NC

Charles E. Merrill Publishing Co.
A Bell & Howell Company
Columbus, Ohio
Toronto • London • Sydney

Series Editor: Terry B. Flohr
Editors: Joyce T. Spangler, Janet Helenthal
Cover Design: Patricia Cohan
Artists: Lynn Norton, Beth Ann Clingan, Mark D. Clingan
Production Editor: Joy E. Dickerson

ISBN 0-675-07097-X

Published by
Charles E. Merrill Publishing Co.
A Bell & Howell Company
Columbus, Ohio 43216

Printed in the United States of America

Preface

Principles of Science: Activity-Centered Program, Teacher's Guide assists the teacher in conducting an activity-oriented science program where observation and experimentation are stressed. An activity-oriented approach gives students the opportunity to investigate and discover scientific concepts. Thus, students are able to improve their investigative skills.

This guide is particularly useful in classrooms where extensive laboratory facilities and equipment are not available. The activities require only simple and inexpensive equipment. Practical suggestions for setting up an efficient and safe laboratory program are given. The guide also includes instructions for obtaining supplies and constructing apparatus. Teaching strategies that are appropriate in a variety of classroom situations are also included.

Each activity is identified by its title and page number in *Principles of Science, Book Two*. The guide includes some teacher demonstrations and extensions for selected activities in the student's text. Additional activities are also provided. Included in each chapter of the Guide is a laboratory activity entitled "Challenge: Applying Scientific Methods." These activities are designed to challenge more highly-motivated students.

It is important to note that not all activity work takes place in the science classroom. Field trips should be included in an activity-oriented approach. Information in this Guide concerning field trips explains how to organize and use field studies as teaching tools.

TABLE OF CONTENTS

INTRODUCTION

UNIT 1   HUMAN LIFE

chapter 1   Science and Technology

chapter 2   The Human Body

chapter 3   Circulatory Systems

chapter 4   Internal Body Processes

chapter 5 Nervous and Endocrine Systems

UNIT 2 HUMAN HEALTH

chapter 6 Nutrition

chapter 7 Disease

chapter 8 Drugs

chapter 9 Human Reproduction and Heredity

UNIT 3 CHEMISTRY

chapter 10 Matter

chapter 11   Elements

chapter 12   Reactions

chapter 13   Chemical Technology

UNIT 4   ENERGY

chapter 14   Heat

chapter 15   Sound and Light

chapter 16   Magnetism and Electricity

chapter 17   Nuclear Energy

UNIT 5   ASTRONOMY
chapter 18   Astronomy and the Moon

chapter 19   Our Solar System

INTRODUCTION

Principles of Science: Activity-Centered Program, Teacher's Guide is designed to help maximize student involvement in activities. Suggestions in this guide are also designed to simplify your preparation and supervision of the activities.

Principles of Science: Teacher's Annotated Edition lists the materials and equipment needed for all activities on pages 30T-34T. Try to consult the list and have the necessary equipment ready prior to the time it is needed. Some additional activities will require materials not listed in the *Teacher's Annotated Edition.* If any activity calls for tools, for rearrangement of furniture, or for the construction of simple equipment, be sure to check with the proper school authorities. Information on how to prepare the solutions used in the activities can be found on pages 34T and 35T of the *Principles of Science: Teacher's Annotated Edition.* A list of suppliers is also provided on page 34T.

Format of this Book

Text activities and additional activities not found in the text are included in this guide. Some additional activities are recommended as teacher demonstrations. These activities may be unsuitable for an entire class to perform due to safety factors or to cost, or because students would gain more from observing the activities than from performing them. However, you must make the final decision as to whether you present demonstrations or your students perform the activities.

At the end of each chapter is an activity labeled "Challenge: Applying Scientific Methods." Challenge activities are designed to challenge your more motivated students. These exercises emphasize inference and other higher learning processes. In these exercises, students often must apply a concept presented in the chapter to a new situation. Other exercises expand on concepts introduced in the text. Challenge activities are geared specifically for highly motivated and interested students. Thus, you may not want to assign this activity to all students.

Each activity in the *Activity Centered Program Teacher's Guide* follows the format outlined here.

ACTIVITY TITLE, NUMBER, AND PAGE:

Each activity has a number and title that corresponds to the number and title appearing in *Principles of Science*. The page number reference indicates the page on which this activity appears in the text.

OBJECTIVE:

The objective provides a statement that briefly describes the purpose of each activity. When the purpose of an activity is clear, students are able to use their time wisely.

CLASS TIME ALLOTMENT:

The approximate amount of class time needed for an average class to complete the activity is indicated here. This time refers to the amount of time it takes students to set up the apparatus and perform the activity only. It does not include teacher preparation time or time for students to answer the questions provided.

MATERIALS:

A complete list of materials needed to conduct the activity is included here. Equipment substitutes are often listed when applicable. Activities may require the preassembly of certain equipment prior to class. Students may be requested to bring certain items from home.

PREPARATION NOTES:

This section provides suggestions for setting up and performing the activity. Additional background information about the concept presented in the activity also may be provided.

PROCEDURE:

A step-by-step listing of the procedure is included in this section. You may want to discuss the procedures before students begin the activity. This discussion may help prevent the misuse of equipment and prevent injuries that can result from the careless use of glassware, burners, and chemicals.

OBSERVATIONS AND DATA:

This section will provide expected observations. It also will provide sample measurements, graphs, charts, and tables to help improve students' recording and organizational skills. Emphasis should be placed on the need to record all observations during and at the completion of an activity. In many cases, this recorded data provides the necessary link between cause and effect relationships. Sample data are included for some activities.

QUESTIONS AND CONCLUSIONS:

Questions found in this section are designed to review the main ideas of the activity, to direct attention to key parts of the procedure, and to relate material to science concepts and skills. Answers directly follow each question and are printed in italics.

ADDITIONAL QUESTIONS:

Discussion questions and their answers are included in this section. The questions and their answers promote and reinforce student learning. It is recommended that the questions be reviewed in class after students have been given time to answer them. This review allows you to spot unclear thinking and to correct it immediately.

EXTENSION:

Extensions are provided for some activities in this guide. They may be suggested additional procedures or demonstrations that extend the material in the student's text. These extension ideas may be assigned as outside projects or can be completed in class after the original activity is performed. They may also provide a different approach to setting up or conducting the activity described in the text.

Using the Guide

You may effectively use different methods in carrying out the activities in *Principles of Science.* Therefore, use the methods best suited to your class sizes, resources, and student ability levels. Some activities may be completed by students individually in class or at home. Other activities may be performed in class in small groups of two to four students. Certain activities should be demonstrated for the class by yourself or appointed students, depending on the complexity of the activity and your students' abilities. Whatever method you use, stress the investigative approach. That is, carry out the activity in such a way that students test their hypotheses by making observations and then drawing conclusions.

Before students begin an activity, introduce the topic and the problem to be investigated. The introduction should cover identification of any unfamiliar materials needed (if necessary), the techniques involved in the procedure, and all applicable safety procedures. You may also include a discussion of the hypotheses involved. However, it is particularly important to avoid telling students "what will happen." Avoid a discussion of what observations to look for and what conclusions to draw until the activity is completed. Remind students to observe closely during the actual activity and record all of their observations. This will give students practice in separating nonessential clues when they use their data to draw conclusions.

Often the observations and conclusions of the students may differ with the suggested observations and conclusions. This situation becomes an excellent "teachable moment," allowing you to lead a discussion to clarify or expand student thinking. At other times, an activity may not go as expected. This too can be a teachable moment in which you and your students diagnose the problem and offer possible solutions. When classroom activities fail to work as anticipated, it is usually because of one of the following reasons: (1) a substance, chemical, or solution was inadvertently omitted, (2) the concentration or amount of a material used was too great or too small, or (3) the apparatus was not properly assembled. When electric appliances fail to operate, first check to see if the appliance has a defective plug; next, see if there is a burned-out bulb or switch and then see if the power is off.

The educational value of any activity may be increased through a post-activity discussion in which the main points of the activity are reviewed and/or clarified. Pertinent questions can be asked and answered by both you and your students. This is part of the scientific process, exchanging data and ideas about a hypothesis.

Evaluating Activity Work

Evaluation of the activities and of the general outcomes of laboratory work is a difficult task. Pure recognition and recall tests are not usually suitable for evaluating laboratory experience. Evaluation methods that depend upon accurate observation, recognition of pertinent data, and ability to reason logically are more suitable for measuring outcomes of laboratory work. Students should keep records of their work in notebooks in a format that allows for easy review and checking. An outline can help students organize information. A recommended outline has the following headings.

NAME:
DATE:
ACTIVITY TITLE:
OBJECTIVE:
OBSERVATIONS AND DATA:
CONCLUSIONS:
QUESTIONS AND ANSWERS:

You may wish to have students include the steps in the Procedure for each activity. If copying facilities are available, you may want to design an activity report outline and distribute it to your students. Students should list the activity title and objective before they begin the activity. Any table for organizing data should be set up at this time.

Appropriate credit for activity work should be incorporated into the assigned grade for the class. Many students who have average performances on paper and pencil evaluations demonstrate exceptional aptitude and achievement in activity work. Student notebooks are one good indicator of activity performance. Periodic checking of the notebooks helps to keep them current and complete. Activity practical tests is another method of evaluation that can demonstrate the student's proficiency in basic laboratory skills. You may wish to design such a test to cover the basic laboratory techniques described later in this guide.

An observational checklist based on behavioral objectives for an activity is another method of skills evaluation. A sample checklist for evaluating general laboratory methods is shown below. The numbers used within the chart should indicate the following: 1—student is careless, 2—student needs improvement, 3—student is proficient. Checklists such as this can be copied on small file cards and kept for each student.

NAME_____	CLASS_____
SKILL	**DATE** 9/22
Handles the balance properly	2
Reads volume from a graduated cylinder	2
Reads the balance correctly	1
Handles a thermometer correctly	2
Measures length accurately	3
Cleans the lab area after an activity	2
Follows the procedure correctly	3
Observes safe lab techniques	1

Sample Laboratory Report

NAME: Donald Raphael

DATE: 3/25/

ACTIVITY TITLE: Finding Area

OBJECTIVE: To learn how to calculate area of an object.

OBSERVATIONS: Area is calculated by multiplying length times width. Area can be calculated for flat surfaces by first measuring length and width of the surface.

	3.8	2.0	7.6	38	20	760
	2.5	1.5	3.75	25	15	375

CONCLUSION: Area is calculated by multiplying length time width. Area is always reported in square units (example cm^2 or mm^2)

QUESTIONS AND ANSWERS:

1. Explain how one finds area of an object.
   Measure length and width of the object. Multiply the two numbers together to get area.

2. What type of units are used to express area if one measures in
   (a) millimeters?   square millimeters or mm^2
   (b) centimeters?   square centimeters or cm^2
   (c) meters?   square meters or m^2

3. How many square millimeters equal a square centimeter?   100

4. How can you convert
   (a) square millimeters to square centimeters?   divide by 100
   (b) square centimeters to square millimeters?   multiply by 100

5. Record the following information for object A.
   (a) length in centimeters   3   (d) length in millimeters   30
   (b) width in centimeters   1.7   (e) width in millimeters   17
   (c) area in centimeters square   5.1   (f) area in millimeters square   510

Laboratory Design and Equipment

Sufficient work space is essential in operating an activity-oriented science program. Both a demonstration table and space for students to work in small groups are needed. A portable laboratory demonstration cart is useful if the science classroom lacks a demonstration table and utilities. These carts are available from several scientific suppliers. They usually contain work space, a sink, a gas torch or burner, water reservoirs, and storage cabinets. See Figure 1. One advantage of the portable demonstration cart is that it can be moved to any location in the classroom and from room to room for science instruction. It can also be used in a large room for instructing groups.

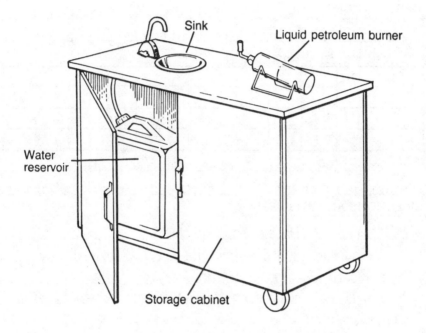

FIGURE 1

FIGURE 1

Equipment may be stored in cabinets or in labeled cartons. Cardboard shoe boxes and plastic dishpans make good storage cabinets that stack neatly. You can probably obtain a good supply of shoe boxes from local shoe stores. You may store bottles, test tubes, wire, and so forth in separate labeled containers. However; if an adequate supply of equipment is available, you may want to organize it in kits. Each kit should contain an equipment checklist as shown in Figure 2. Each team of students would be responsible for filling out and returning this checklist to you at specific intervals, such as once a month or once each semester. These lists will not only enable you to keep track of materials and breakage, but also to assess students' proficiency in keeping their equipment clean and organized.

FIGURE 2

EQUIPMENT CHECKLIST				
Name_____ Date_____				
Quantity	Description	Check in	Check out	Breakage
2	beaker (100 mL)			
2	beaker (250 mL)			
1	beaker (500 mL)			
1	burner			
2	collecting bottles			
2	droppers			

Equipment and specimens that are used only a few times during the year should be labeled and stored in containers in a central location separate from the student kits. Plastic boxes, such as those used to store fishing tackle, work well for small equipment. For larger samples, you can often find inexpensive, divided rubberized trays designed for kitchen use. Plastic cartons used for soft butter, sour cream, and cheese make ideal inexpensive storage containers. Many pharmacies receive supplies in clear plastic boxes and vials that might be saved for you. When equipment is stored in clear containers, the contents can be examined easily without being scattered or damaged. Each container must be clearly labeled as to its contents. Keep a card file of equipment and materials needed for each activity, as shown in Figure 3. These cards will help you determine what materials and equipment are needed ahead of time. It can also help you in ordering materials at the beginning of the school year. You can make notes on the cards of special equipment or materials that may be required or special instructions for the students.

FIGURE 3

ACTIVITY 3-5, page 53 CHANGES IN A BURNING CANDLE	
Materials: Candle Large glass jar Matches Watch glass	**Chemicals:** None

If your supply of laboratory equipment and materials is limited, readily available materials can often be substituted. For example, different sizes of baby food jars can be substituted for beakers. The regular-size jar is about the same size as a 100-mL beaker, while the junior-size jar approximates a 250-mL beaker. Use heat-resistant glassware for heating materials.

You can make the test tube racks from milk cartons by making a series of x-cuts on one side of the carton. A razor blade or scalpel works well in making these x-cuts. Test tubes can then be gently forced into these cuts, Figure 4. Small juice cans or paper cups can also be used to hold test tubes.

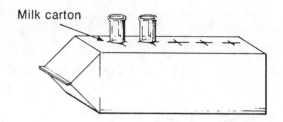

Milk carton

FIGURE 4

Burner stands can be constructed by bending heavy-gauge aluminum wires as shown in Figure 5 and covering the wires with metal screen. Burner stands can also be made from large tin cans cut with tin shears to produce tripods, Figure 5. Care must be taken to avoid the sharp edges of these cans. Bend the edges back toward the inside of the stand.

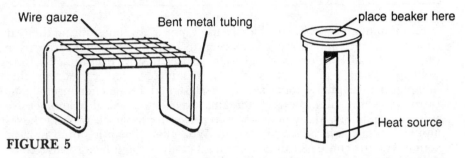

Wire gauze   Bent metal tubing   place beaker here

Heat source

FIGURE 5

Graduated cylinders are needed for measuring liquids. If these cannot be obtained, substitute graduated baby formula bottles (in metric units) or metric measuring cups. You may also use olive jars as graduated cylinders; mark calibrations on a strip of tape using milliliter units, Figure 6. You may, however, mark the lines directly on the glass with a glass-marking pencil. Determine the calibrations by adding a milliliter of water at a time to the olive jar from a standard graduated cylinder.

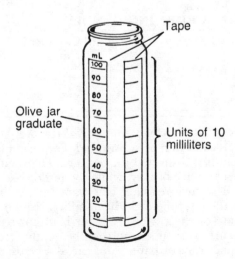

Tape

mL
100
90
80
70
60
50
40
30
20
10

Olive jar graduate

Units of 10 milliliters

FIGURE 6

Storing solutions and chemicals in clearly labeled dropper bottles will reduce spills and waste. Several activities require students to use a few drops of a solution. You may wish to pour the solution into a labeled beaker and provide several droppers for your students. Remind your students that it is important to use a dropper in only one solution. Plastic dropping bottles which dispense only one drop at a time are ideal for those chemicals which should be handled safely (acids or bases). These bottles are available from drug stores or may be collected from discarded prescription eye drop bottles.

Chemical solutions should be prepared prior to the activity only by the teacher. You may wish to prepare enough stock solution to supply several activities. We recommend that your chemical storage areas be limited to teacher access only. Students should not dispense their own chemicals or mix their own solutions from concentrated chemical stock.

If gas outlets for connecting laboratory burners are not present in sufficient numbers for student work, use electric hot plates instead. We do not advocate the use of alcohol burners. Alcohol in the presence of fire is a potentially dangerous situation. Be sure your classroom has an adequate number of electric outlets and use only UL approved extension cords.

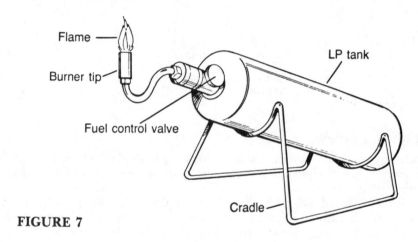

FIGURE 7

For concentrated heat, such as is needed when bending glass, a liquid petroleum burner such as the one shown in Figure 7 is convenient. You may purchase the base and curved burner from a scientific supplier. Replacement fuel tanks are available in hardware and sporting equipment stores.

Laboratory Techniques

Lighting and Adjusting the Flame on a Laboratory Burner

Most laboratory burners have an inlet for gas and a vent or valve for the adjustment of air that is mixed with the gas. For maximum heat, the air gas mixture must be correct. The object to be heated should be placed just above the pale blue part of the flame.

To light the burner, hold a lighted match or a striker next to the barrel of the burner and turn on the gas. See Figure 8. After lighting the burner, adjust the air vent until a light blue cone appears in the center of the flame. If the flame rises from the burner or appears to "blow out" after lighting, reduce the supply of gas. If the flame is yellow, open the air regulator.

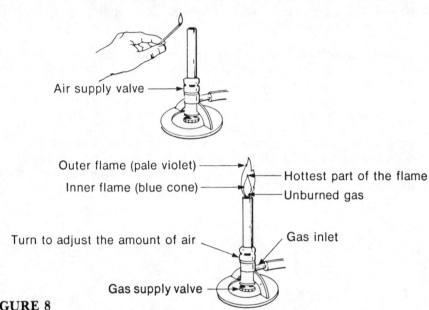

Air supply valve

Outer flame (pale violet) ——————→ Hottest part of the flame

Inner flame (blue cone) ——————— Unburned gas

Turn to adjust the amount of air ——— Gas inlet

Gas supply valve

FIGURE 8

Using the Balance

Although the balance you use may look somewhat different from the balance pictured in Figure 9, all beam balances use similar steps to find an unknown mass.

1. Slide all of the riders back to the zero point. Check to see that the pointer swings freely along the scale an equal distance above and below the zero point. Use the adjustment screw to obtain an equal swing if necessary.

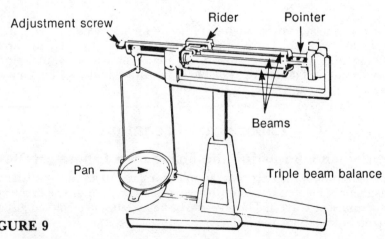

Adjustment screw   Rider   Pointer

Beams

Pan

Triple beam balance

FIGURE 9

2. Never place chemicals directly on the balance. Any dry chemical that is to be massed should be placed on waxed paper or in a glass container.
3. Place the object to be massed on the pan. Move the riders along the beams beginning with the largest mass first. Make sure all riders are in a notch before reading. The pointer need not stop swinging if the swing is an equal distance above and below the zero point on the scale.
4. The mass of the object will be the sum of the masses indicated on the beams.

Decanting and Filtering

It is often necessary to separate a solid from a liquid. Filtration is a common process of separation used in most laboratories. The liquid is decanted, that is, the liquid is separated from the solid by carefully pouring off the liquid leaving only the solid material. To avoid splashing and to maintain control, the liquid is poured down a stirring rod, Figure 10. The solution is usually filtered through filter paper to catch any unsettled solids.

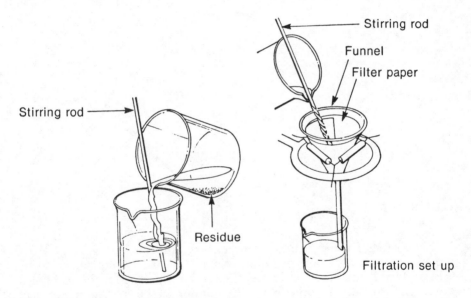

Decanting a liquid from a precipitate

FIGURE 10

Measuring Temperature

When the temperature of a liquid is measured with a thermometer, the bulb of the thermometer should be in the center of the liquid. Do not allow the bulb to touch the sides of the container. When the thermometer is removed from the liquid, the column in the thermometer will soon show the air temperature. For this reason, take temperature readings while the thermometer is in the liquid. When measuring the temperature of hot or boiling liquids, be sure to use a thermometer that is calibrated for high temperatures.

Measuring Volume

The surface of liquids in glass cylinders is often curved. This curved surface is called the meniscus. Most of the liquids you will measure will have a concave meniscus. View the meniscus along a horizontal line of sight. Do not try to make a reading looking up or down at the meniscus. Always read a concave meniscus from the low point of the curve. This measurement gives the most precise volume, because liquids tend to creep up the sides of a glass container. Liquids in many plastic cylinders will not form a meniscus. In such containers, read the volume from the level of the liquid.

Using Chemicals and Reagents

Use a spatula to remove solids from bottles as shown in Figure 11. Always clean the spatula before inserting it into a bottle containing another chemical. Place the solid on a piece of waxed paper. Transfer it to a test tube by folding the paper as shown.

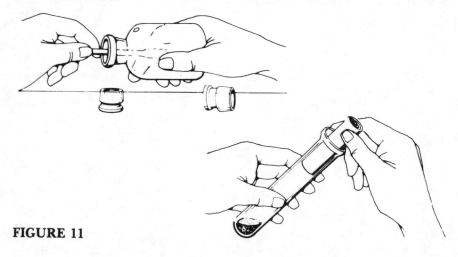

FIGURE 11

Grip the top of a reagent bottle between your fingers. See Figure 12. Hold the bottle top as you pour the liquid. When you wish to dilute an acid, the acid is added to the water, and never the reverse. Slowly pour the acid down the stirring rod and continually stir the solution as shown. Diluting an acid produces heat. Therefore, it is important to add the acid slowly and to stir the solution. We advocate that you not allow students to dilute concentrated acids. You should dilute all acids prior to the activity session.

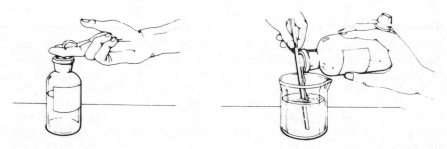

FIGURE 12

When smelling a substance, use a fanning motion to direct the vapor toward you. Never smell a substance directly. The proper technique is shown in Figure 13.

Always point the mouth of the test tube away from yourself and others when you heat the test tube. Move the test tube constantly for even heating. See Figure 13.

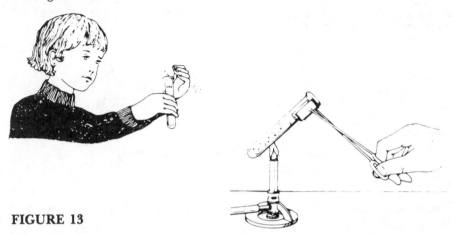

FIGURE 13

Working with Glass Tubing

Figure 14 on this page and continuing on the next page illustrates the proper techniques to use when heating and working with glass tubing. **CAUTION:** Hot glass looks the same as cool glass. Do not touch glass that has been heated until you allow sufficient time for cooling. Always place hot glass on a hot pad, never on a metal or wood desk top. We recommend that you prepare all pieces of glass tubing prior to the activity session.

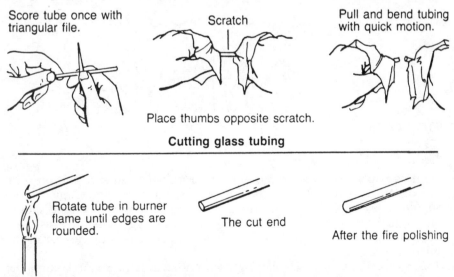

Score tube once with triangular file.

Scratch

Pull and bend tubing with quick motion.

Place thumbs opposite scratch.

Cutting glass tubing

Rotate tube in burner flame until edges are rounded.

The cut end

After the fire polishing

Fire-polishing the ends of cut glass tubing

FIGURE 14

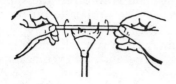

Use a wing tip on burner. Roll the tube back and forth in flame until glass has become soft.

Remove from flame and hold for a few seconds until heat becomes evenly distributed.

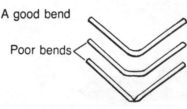

A good bend

Poor bends

Bend quickly and hold until glass hardens.

Proper method of bending glass tubing

Inserting Glass Tubing or a Thermometer into a Stopper

Check the size of the holes in the rubber stopper to see that they are slightly smaller than the tubing or the thermometer. The rubber stopper should stretch enough to hold either firmly.

Place a drop of glycerol on the end of the tubing or thermometer. Glycerol acts as a lubricant. Wrap the glass tubing and the stopper in a cloth towel. Then push the tubing through the stopper using a gentle force and a twisting motion, Figure 15. Never hold the tubing or stopper in such a way that the end of the tubing is pushing against the palm of your hand. If the tubing breaks, it could easily injure your hand.

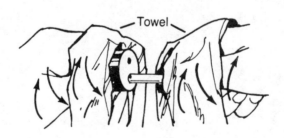

Towel

FIGURE 15

Using a Microscope

Microscopes should be stored in a safe place where storage and retrieval can be supervised by the teacher. If not kept in a cabinet, a microscope should be protected from dust with a cloth or plastic cover. Students should be taught the parts of a microscope (Figure 16) and the proper care, use, and handling of a microscope. Stress the following points about the care of the microscope.

1. Always carry a microscope upright with two hands, one hand holding the arm and one hand supporting the base.
2. Store the microscope with the low power objective (shorter tube) in position.

3. Always bring a specimen into focus with the low power objective. Then, if necessary, switch to high power.
4. Never use coarse adjustment (large knob) to focus the high power objective.
5. When using the coarse adjustment to lower the low power objective, always look at the microscope from the side. If you look through the eyepiece, you may accidently force the objective into the coverslip.
6. Do not allow direct sunlight to fall on the mirror and reflect up into the eye.
7. Clean lenses only with lens paper. Moisten the lens paper with a drop of water or alcohol if the lens does not wipe clean with dry lens paper.
8. Be careful when using coverslips and microscope slides because they may crack or shatter when dropped.

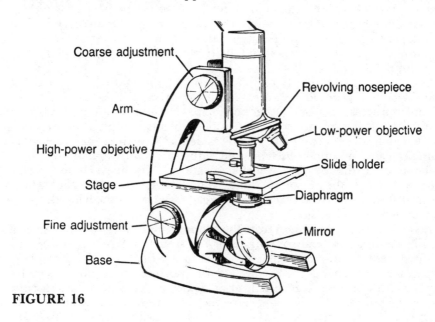

FIGURE 16

Care of Living Material

Life science teaching can contribute to the development of respect for life through the application of humane principles in the educational use of living organisms. Students should be taught the importance of providing good care for pets, animals used in class, and animals used in science projects. Students should not conduct activities which cause pain, hardship, or death to animals. It is recommended that all activities and projects involving living organisms be conducted with care, discretion, and respect for living organisms.

The teacher should discourage students from bringing in any living material unless there is a proper place to keep it and a designated person to take care of it. However, if there are adequate facilities for students to have animals in school, this would be a good opportunity for students to learn how to care for and preserve life. Pets and laboratory animals should be given adequate ventilation, proper sanitary conditions, fresh water daily, and a balanced diet. Teachers should make provisions for the proper care of classroom plants and animals during weekends and vacation periods. In most cases, the school custodian will handle these chores when requested courteously and given proper directions. Plants and animals may be taken home by responsible students during school vacation periods. At these times be certain to provide simple written instructions for the care of living material. Instructions may be taped to containers left in the classroom or taken home by students.

Field Trips

Field studies are often used to extend student interest and knowledge in science. A good field trip can help students see the relationship of science to their lives more than all the reading they do in a text. The success of a field trip depends on careful preparation both by you and your students. To organize and conduct a successful field trip, the following suggestions may be helpful.

Evaluate your community for possible field trip opportunities. A police crime laboratory would be an excellent opportunity for students to see scientific processes at work. Other possibilities include nuclear power plants, fossil fuel power plants, water treatment plants, hospital laboratories, construction sites for commercial and residential structures, natural history museums, and museums of science and industry. As you evaluate your area, make a card file of the available locations. Try to include specific information as to the person to contact, hours the site is open, what facilities are available on-site (restrooms, places to eat, facilities for the handicapped), and directions to the site.

Request written permission from the proper school authorities and keep it on file. Arrange for transportation for the students. When permission is granted, send a written statement of where the field trip will take place, departure and arrival times, method of transportation, and necessary expenditures (if any) to each parent or guardian. Provide a place for the parent or guardian to sign and have the form returned to you.

Discuss the proper procedures for a field trip with your students. Each field trip should have specific learning objectives correlated to the lesson and text material. Make certain that students understand the purpose of the field trip. Do not try to crowd too much into one field trip.

Tell your students what equipment to bring and what specific dress requirements (if any) exist. Students may bring pencils, paper, and cameras (with proper clearance). If the trip is to a museum or a guided tour of an industrial plant, some students may wish to bring tape recorders. Check with the person on-site to be sure this is acceptable. Before visiting a museum or plant, give students a chance to discuss the kinds of behavior acceptable in a formal situation. The discussion might include the need for quiet, courtesy, and observation of all rules of the site.

Field trips to industries call for the greatest amount of formality. Students will usually be conducted through as a group. Usually, individuals will not be free to go to different places away from the group. They will be expected to keep the same pace as the leader. This procedure should be pointed out to students before they enter the building. Many industries have tight security with guides to see that everyone follows the rules of the company.

Nature trips are an important activity for science students. Students should be briefed on the purpose of the trip. They should be instructed as to what specimens they will be allowed to collect at the site. Background information should be given before starting the trip. Once at the site, encourage students to make their own observations.

To follow up the field trip, have students discuss their experiences and exchange ideas. Encourage them to ask questions and propose future activities related to the field trip. Schedule individual or group reports to evaluate the field trip.

Safety in the Laboratory

The activities in the *Principles of Science* program are designed to minimize dangers in the laboratory. Even so, there are no guarantees against accidents. However, careful planning and preparation as well as being aware of hazards can help keep accidents to a minimum. The following guidelines can help you maintain a safe laboratory. This list is by no means complete. Consult the National Science Teachers Association, 1742 Connecticut Ave. N.W., Washington, DC 20009 for additional publications concerning safety in the science classroom.

General Safety: General safety rules are listed in the Appendices of *Principles of Science,* and on the following page. These general rules should be emphasized to students before any laboratory work is done, and also should be periodically reviewed. Stress to students the importance of adhering to these rules to ensure their own safety as well as the safety of others.

Additional Safety Guidelines: The additional guidelines and suggestions listed below will further aid you in making the laboratory a safe place to work and learn.

Before Each Activity:
(1) Perform activities yourself before assigning them to students to determine where students may have trouble.
(2) Arrange the laboratory in such a way so that equipment and supplies are easily accessible to students. Avoid confusion where solutions and reagents are dispensed.
(3) Have available only equipment and supplies needed to complete the assigned activity. This practice helps eliminate the problem of students doing unauthorized experiments.
(4) Review the procedures with students and emphasize cautions found within the procedure.
(5) Be sure all students know proper procedures to follow if an accident should occur.

During the Activity:
(1) Make sure that the laboratory is clean and free of clutter.
(2) Students should wear goggles and aprons when heating substances or working with chemicals that can cause burns.
(3) Never allow students to work alone in the laboratory.
(4) Never allow students to use a scalpel or other cutting device with more than one edge.
(5) If your microscopes require a separate light source, be sure students use proper lamps. Using reflected sunlight can damage the eye.

(6) Use extreme caution if you use a pressure cooker for sterilization purposes. Turn off the heat source, remove the cooker, and allow the pressure to return to normal before opening the cover.

(7) Students should never point the open end of a heated test tube toward anyone.

(8) Remove broken or chipped glassware from use immediately. Also clean up any spills that occur immediately. Dilute concentrated solutions with water before removing.

(9) Be sure that all glassware that is to be heated is a heat treated type that will not shatter.

(10) Remind students that heated glassware looks cool several seconds after heating, but can still burn for several minutes.

After the Activity:
(1) Be sure that the laboratory is clean. Clean all work surfaces and equipment.

(2) Be certain that students have disposed of chemicals and broken glassware properly.

(3) Be sure all hot plates and burners are off before leaving the laboratory.

Safety Rules

1. Do not perform activities that are unauthorized. Always obtain your teacher's permission.

2. Study your assignment. If you are in doubt about any procedure, ask your teacher for help.

3. Use the safety equipment provided for you. Know the location of the fire extinguisher, safety shower, fire blanket, first aid kit, phone, fire alarm, and the nurse.

4. Safety glasses and safety apron should be worn when any activity calls for heating, pouring, or mixing of chemicals.

5. Report any accident, injury, or incorrect procedure to your teacher at once.

6. Smother fires with a towel. If clothing should catch fire, smother it with a blanket or coat or quench it under a safety shower. **NEVER RUN.**

7. Handle chemicals and bend glassware only under the direction of your teacher. If you spill acid or another corrosive chemical, wash it off immediately with water. Never taste any chemical substance or draw poisonous materials into a glass tube with your mouth. Never inhale chemicals. Keep combustible materials away from open flames.

8. Place broken glass and solid substances in designated containers. Keep insoluble waste material out of the sink.

9. When your activity is completed, be sure to turn off the water and gas and disconnect electrical connections. Clean your work area. Return all materials to their proper places.

First Aid

INJURY	SAFE RESPONSE
burns	Flush with water. Call your teacher immediately.
cuts and bruises	Follow the instructions in the first aid kit. Report to the school nurse.
fainting or collapse	Provide the person with fresh air. Have the person recline so that their head is lower than their body. Call your teacher. A nurse or a doctor may be needed to provide artificial respiration.
fire	Wrap person in fire blanket. Extinguish all flames.
foreign matter in eye	Flush with plenty of water. Use eyewash bottle or fountain.
poisoning	Note the suspected poisoning agent and call your teacher.
severe bleeding	Apply pressure or a compress directly to the wound and get medical attention.

spills on skin
  acid spills
  base spills
	Flush with water or use safety shower.
	Apply baking soda and call your teacher.
	Apply boric acid and call your teacher.

UNIT ONE

Human Life

chapter 1
Science and Technology

ACTIVITY 1-1: Making Observations (page 8)

OBJECTIVE: To test and compare your powers of observation

CLASS TIME ALLOTMENT: 15 minutes.

MATERIALS:

paper   pencil

PREPARATION NOTES:

In this activity the student uses illustrations to help understand the concepts of qualitative and quantitative observations. Call student's attention to the need for accuracy in making observations in fields such as science, journalism, and sports.

PROCEDURE:

1. Look at the photograph on pages 2-3 of your textbook. Make a list of 10 observations of the photograph.
2. Place a check beside each observation that is quantitative.
3. Compare your observations with those of your classmates.

OBSERVATIONS AND DATA:

Student lists will vary; however, there will be duplicate observations when comparing classroom responses. Similar observations may vary when given a quantitative aspect. This may be due to careless or inaccurate counting or observation. In any experiment, scientists repeat their observations so that if an error does occur, it becomes less significant when included among many correct observations.

QUESTIONS AND CONCLUSIONS:

1. How many students made the same observations you did?   *Answers will vary.*
2. Do you have different observations?   *Answers will vary.*
3. What might be a reason for the differences in observations?   *Careless observation, error in counting, change in numbers of objects from moment to moment.*

ADDITIONAL QUESTIONS:

4. Might ten scientists performing the same experiment all observe the same results?   *no*
5. A quantitative observation is one that includes a number.
   (a) Did your list include any quantitative observations?   *Answers will vary.*
   (b) Give an example of a quantitative observation.   *1 clock, 8 lanes*
   (c) Are quantitative observations more or less specific than those without a number?   *more specific*

ACTIVITY 1-2: Measuring (page 11)

OBJECTIVE: To gain experience in measuring

CLASS TIME ALLOTMENT: 30 minutes.

MATERIALS:

baby food jar	graduated cylinder, 100 mL	nail
balance	ice cube	paper clip
beaker, 250 mL	metric ruler	pencil
Celsius thermometer	milk carton, empty	stirring rod
		water

PREPARATION NOTES:

In this activity the student gains experience measuring with metric units. The use of a plastic collar on a graduated cylinder will prevent breakage if it is knocked over. Have students copy the data table into their notebooks before they begin work. Also review safety factors, discipline rules, and procedures for distribution and retrieval of materials.

PROCEDURE:

1. Copy the data table into your notebook.
2. Measure the length of the nail, paper clip, and pencil in millimeters. Record the results in your data table.
3. Measure the length of the three objects in Step 2 in centimeters and record.
4. Use the balance to measure the mass of the three objects in Step 2 and record.
5. Use the graduated cylinder and measure the volume of the baby food jar and the milk carton. Record these volumes.
6. Determine and record the mass of the empty graduated cylinder.
7. Determine and record the mass of the graduate containing 10 mL water.

8. Pour 100 mL water into the beaker and record the water temperature.
9. Place an ice cube in the water and stir until the ice is gone. Record the temperature of the water again.

OBSERVATIONS AND DATA:

Sample measurements are given in the teacher's edition on text page 11. These measurements are used to answer the Questions and Conclusions section. Student data may vary from this data, depending on the materials used.

QUESTIONS AND CONCLUSIONS:

1. How much longer than the paper clip was the pencil?   *14.5 cm*
2. Which had the greater mass, the nail or the paper clip?   *nail*
3. What was the volume of the baby food jar? The milk carton?   *Answers will vary.*
4. Calculate the mass of 1 mL of water.   *about 1.0 g*
5. What effect did the ice cube have on the temperature of the water?   *lowered the water temperature.*

EXTENSION:

If commercial balances are not available, students may construct their own from inexpensive materials. Use the following procedures for assembling and using a student-made balance.

1. Assemble as follows:
   (a) Tape 4 straws together along their center.
   (b) Use a small strip of a file card to form a cradle for the 4 straws.
   (c) Push a needle through the card. Make sure that the straws fit snug inside the card cradle. Reposition the needle if necessary.
   (d) Cut a notch at the ends of the top straw. Make sure that the notch is equidistant from each end.
   (e) Secure bottle caps with tape and thread so that they hang from each notch.
   (f) Cut a liter milk carton in half. Use each half to support the needle.

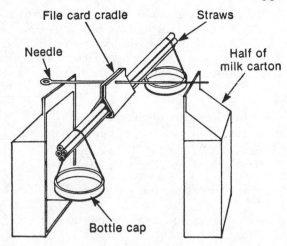

FILE card cradle   Straws
Needle   Half of milk carton
Bottle cap

FIGURE 1-1

2. Using the balance
   (a) If both caps (pans) do not come to rest evenly, slide the paper card slightly to the left or right until a balance is achieved.
   (b) Place objects of known mass on the right pan. A paper clip can be used by students as a standard: 1 paper clip (size no. 1) = 0.6 g.
   (c) Place the object, such as a penny, to be massed on the left pan. Add enough paper clips on the other pan until they balance. Determine the mass of the penny as follows. Count the number of paper clips used to almost balance one penny. Multiply the number of clips used by 0.6 g (1 clip = 0.6 grams). EXAMPLE: 1 penny = 5 clips × 0.6 g = 3.0 grams
3. Have students compare their values for a penny. (Correct answers should be close to 5 clips.) Discuss why student answers may vary. Possible reasons are:
   (a) Wrong count of clips.
   (b) Each clip may differ slightly in mass.
   (c) Balance only allows masses in units of 0.6 g. Fractional parts of 0.6 g cannot be determined if paper clips are used.
4. A graph converting clips to grams may be designed as follows to reduce math errors and to easily determine the mass of other objects while using paper clips as a comparison.

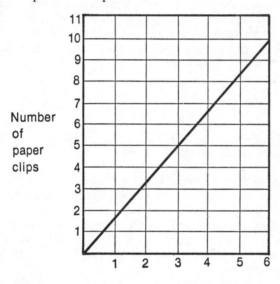

Number of paper clips

FIGURE 1-2   Grams

5. Determine the mass in paper clips of a nickel and a dime. Convert to grams using graph or multiplying numbers of clips by 0.6 g.
6. Have students record data in a chart similar to the following.

	MASS IN PAPER CLIPS	**MASS IN GRAMS**	**MASS IN MILLIGRAMS**
Penny			
Nickel			
Dime			

7. If kilogram concept is desired, add a new column to chart and discuss need for dividing grams by 1000 to get kilograms.

ACTIVITY 1-3: Science and Technology on Television
(page 13)

OBJECTIVE: To observe and record examples of science and technology seen on television programs

CLASS TIME ALLOTMENT: 15 minutes.

MATERIALS:

television

weekly television guide

PREPARATION NOTES:

In this activity the student observes examples of science and technology while watching television. The purpose of the activity is to help students gain an awareness of science and technology in their daily lives. When assigning this activity, use a weekly television guide to identify programs related to science and technology. Students should log the program, day and time, channel, and examples of science and technology. NOTE: This activity should be done at home.

PROCEDURE:

1. Before sitting down to watch television, have a clear meaning of the assignment, and paper and pencil ready.
2. While watching a particular program, record the following: name of the program, date of program, time of program.
3. List examples seen in the program that illustrate a use of science (biology, chemistry, physics). More than one area of science may apply to the same program.
4. List under the area of science the examples that illustrate technology in that science area. For example, under physics, use of radar, walkie-talkie radios; under engineering, farm equipment, rocket ships; under biology, powerful new insecticides, etc.
5. Commercial messages may also be used to illustrate science and technology as well as the program itself.

OBSERVATIONS AND DATA:

Many shows and commercials use some area of science. Frequently the entire story line is directed to some technical aspect or breakthrough of science.

QUESTIONS AND CONCLUSIONS:

The most important conclusion from this activity is how science and technology do indeed influence our daily lives, not as seen on television, but actually during our own daily activities.

1. What are three areas of science?   *chemistry, biology, physics*
2. What is meant by technology?   *the application of science for practical purposes*
3. Is technology used often in our daily lives?   *yes* Give some examples. *microwave ovens, personal computers, calculators, CB radios, solar water heaters*

CHALLENGE: APPLYING SCIENTIFIC METHODS
Making a Hypothesis

OBJECTIVE: To investigate how a scientist makes and revises a hypothesis

CLASS TIME ALLOTMENT: 30 minutes.

MATERIALS:

chemical A (NaOH)	test tube	water
chemical B (NH_4NO_3)	test tube rack	
graduated cylinder	thermometer	

PREPARATION NOTES:

In this activity the student is asked to make a best guess about the problem, "How does the temperature of water change as chemicals are added to it?" The student then performs an experiment to check his or her hypothesis. Data is collected and used in reaching a final hypothesis. You may wish to suggest possible hypotheses to students such as temperature rising, falling, or remaining unchanged as chemicals are added.

PROCEDURE:

1. Write your hypothesis of "best guess" about the following problem, "How does the temperature of water change as chemicals are added?

Part A
1. Add 5 mL of water to a test tube.
2. Place the tube into a test tube rack. Put a thermometer into the water. Wait 1 minute and then record the starting temperature. Do not remove the thermometer.
3. Use a spoon to add 3 small pellets of chemical A to the test tube. Note the time. CAUTION: Do not touch pellets with your hands.
4. Read the water temperature every 15 seconds and record as Trial 1.
5. Continue taking the water temperature every 15 seconds for a total of 2 minutes.
6. Pour the contents of the test tube into a sink and rinse the sink with water.
7. Repeat steps 1 through 6 and record as Trial 2. Total and record an average for each time/temperature reading.

Part B
1. Add 5 mL water to a clean test tube and record its starting temperature.
2. Add one-half spoonful of chemical B to the tube.
3. Record the temperature of the water for every 15 seconds as Trial 1.
4. Repeat steps 1 through 3 and record as Trial 2. Total and record an average temperature for each time period.

OBSERVATIONS AND DATA:

Student data will vary. However, data should show that chemical A increases water temperature, and chemical B decreases it.

	STARTING TEMPER-ATURE OF WATER (°C)	TEMPERATURE AFTER ADDING CHEMICAL A (°C)							
		TIME IN SECONDS							
		15	30	45	60	75	90	105	120
Trial 1	22	22	23	25	26	26	25	25	24
Trial 2	22	22	23	24	26	28	27	27	27
Total	44	44	46	49	52	54	52	52	51
Average	22	22	23	24.5	26	27	26	26	25.5

	STARTING TEMPER-ATURE OF WATER (°C)	TEMPERATURE AFTER ADDING CHEMICAL B (°C)							
		TIME IN SECONDS							
		15	30	45	60	75	90	105	120
Trial 1	22	22	21	20	19	18	17	17	18
Trial 2	22	21	20	19	18	18	18	17	19
Total	44	43	41	39	37	36	35	34	37
Average	22	21.5	20.5	19.5	18.5	18	17.5	17	18.5

QUESTIONS AND CONCLUSIONS:

1. (a) According to your average results, what happened to your water temperature when chemical A was added?   *Water temperature increased.*
   (b) According to your average results, what happened to your water temperature when chemical B was added?   *Water temperature decreased.*
2. Do all chemicals cause water temperature to change in the same way?   *no*
3. Look at your original hypothesis before starting the experiment. Was your original hypothesis correct?   *Answers will vary.*
4. If your original hypothesis was not correct, write a new correct hypothesis.   *Different chemicals may cause the water temperature to either increase or decrease.*
5. (a) Why is a hypothesis called a best guess?   *It is an answer that is based on what you believe is correct.*
   (b) What must scientists do before accepting their best guess?   *They must test their hypothesis by performing experiments.*

Student data may be graphed if time permits. Graph average temperature on the vertical axis and time intervals on the horizontal axis.

---

chapter 2

The Human Body

ACTIVITY 2-1: Lung Capacities (page 21)

OBJECTIVE: To compare lung capacities

CLASS TIME ALLOTMENT: One period.

MATERIALS:

beaker (250 mL)	rubber tubing (50 cm)
dishpan	water
graduated cylinder (100 mL)	wood blocks (3, same size)
marking pencil	alcohol for sterilizing mouth piece
jar/lid (4-6 L)	paper towels

PREPARATION NOTES:

In this activity the student measures and compares the lung capacities of class members. Caution students to be careful in using water and to keep all water in the containers provided. The area of tubing put in the mouth should be sterilized with alcohol, rinsed with water, and dried each time it is used. The level of water may be marked with a pencil or a piece of tape. After the students have completed the activity, go over the steps involved in making a bar graph. Have students complete the bar graph drawings and then go over the Questions and Conclusions.

PROCEDURE:

1. Fill the dishpan half full of water. Place the wood blocks on the bottom.
2. Completely fill the jar with water and tighten the lid.
3. Hold the jar over the dishpan, turn it upside down and set it in the dishpan.
4. Keeping the mouth of the jar underwater, remove the lid. Place the jar on the wood blocks (Figure 2-2). Be careful not to lift the mouth of the jar above water.
5. Slide one end of the rubber tubing into the jar. Be careful to keep the other end of the tubing higher than the dishpan at all times.
6. *Inhale* deeply, taking as much air into your lungs as you can. Then *exhale* all the air in your lungs through the rubber tubing.
7. Mark the level of water with the marking pencil after you have exhaled into the jar. Label the mark with your initials.
8. Repeat Steps 6 and 7 for several of your classmates. Mark each water level and label it with each student's initials.

9. Remove the jar from the dishpan and empty the water.
10. Use the graduate to fill the jar to the first mark with water. Record the volume. Without emptying the jar, add water to the next mark using the graduate. Record this amount. Continue adding water and recording until all volumes have been recorded. Recorded volumes are a measure of each person's lung capacity.

OBSERVATIONS AND DATA:

Student lung capacities will vary with size, health, and other factors. The average for males of the student's age would be 3.7 to 4.2 L. The average for females of student's age would be 3.1 to 3.4 L. Height and weight are the determining factors for lung capacity.

QUESTIONS AND CONCLUSIONS:

1. What was your lung capacity?   *Answers will vary.*
2. Did everyone have the same capacity?   *No, there will be variations related to size, health, and other factors.*
3. What was the largest lung capacity? the smallest? the average?   *Answers will vary.*
4. From your data, what can you conclude about the lung capacities of males versus females in your class?   *Generally, the average lung capacity for males is greater than for females.*

ACTIVITY 2-2: Human Cells (page 25)

OBJECTIVE: To observe human cheek cells using a microscope

CLASS TIME ALLOTMENT: 20 minutes.

MATERIALS:

dropper   microscope slide/coverslip
microscope   toothpick
iodine solution   water

PREPARATION NOTES:

In this activity the student observes epithelial cheek cells and identifies the cell membrane, nucleus, and cytoplasm in one such cheek cell. Point out the proper procedure for placing a coverslip on a wet mount. The coverslip is held vertically alongside the water with one edge on the surface of the slide. Capillary action allows the water to close the edge between the slide and coverslip. Then the coverslip is tilted until the water is covered. This procedure reduces the chance of air bubbles being trapped under the coverslip. If air bubbles do occur, gently tap the coverslip with your fingernail until the bubbles are gone. Explain to the students that many of the cell structures shown in Figure 2-3 can only be seen with an electron microscope that magnifies the cell several thousand times.

PROCEDURE:

1. Place a drop of water in the center of the slide.
2. Gently scrape the inside lining of your cheek with one end of the toothpick. Stir that end of the toothpick in the drop of water. Put the toothpick into a trash container.

3. Use the dropper to add a drop of iodine solution to the water.
4. Place the coverslip on the slide. Place the slide on the stage of the microscope. Focus first using low power and then switch to high power.
5. Observe the cheek cells and sketch a diagram of one as observed under high power.
6. When you have completed your observations, remove the slide, and wash and dry it.

OBSERVATIONS AND DATA:

Refer students to the diagram of a typical cell on page 22 of their text. Students should be able to diagram the following parts of their cell: cell membrane, cytoplasm, and nucleus.

QUESTIONS AND CONCLUSIONS:

1. Why did you mix the cheek cells with water?   *to dilute them so that it will be easier to observe individual cells and their parts.*
2. How did the iodine solution affect the cheek cells?   *It stained the cheek cells.*
3. Describe the cytoplasm.   *Answers will vary. It will appear clear possibly with lumps or grains in it.*
4. Describe the nucleus.   *Answers will vary. It often appears as dark circular or oval body, possibly with a stringy center.*
5. How is a cell different from a tissue? *A tissue is a group of cells working together to perform the same function.*

ADDITIONAL ACTIVITY: The Human Skeleton
(section 2:3)

OBJECTIVE: To identify the bones of the human skeleton using a model or an actual skeleton.

CLASS TIME ALLOTMENT: One period.

MATERIALS:

plastic model of skeleton or actual skeleton, or diagram of skeleton such as the one on p. 26 of **Principles of Science, Book Two**

PREPARATION NOTES: Students will need an actual skeletal model in order to count the number of bones in the wrist, ankle, and skull.

PROCEDURE:

1. Identify the bones on the skeleton using a diagram as a guide.
2. Attempt to match the following list of common bone names with the corresponding technical name.

thigh bone	shoulder blade	ankle bones
kneecap	skull	arm bones
backbone	foot bones	upper arm bone
neck bone	hand bones	breastbone
leg bones	toes	collarbone
wrist bone	pelvis	lower jaw
ribs		

Record your observations in Steps 3-6 in the chart provided. (Put this chart on the board for students.)

3. Count the number of wrist bones.
   Count the number of ankle bones.
4. Count the number of finger and hand bones.
   Count the number of toe and foot bones.
5. Count the number of ribs present. Examine the ribs and determine if all are connected to the backbone. Examine the ribs and determine if all are connected to the breastbone.
6. Count the number of bones fused to form the skull.

OBSERVATIONS AND DATA:

BODY PART	NUMBER OF BONES
Wrist	8
Ankle	7
Finger and hand	5 metacarpals 14 phalanges
Toe and foot	5 metatarsals 14 phalanges
Ribs	24
Skull	cranium 8 face 14

QUESTIONS AND CONCLUSIONS:

1. How are the human ankle and wrist similar?   *They have the same type of bones. The wrist has eight small bones, and the ankle has seven.*
2. How are the foot and hand similar?   *They have the same number of bones.*
3. How are the toe and finger similar?   *They have the same number of bones.*
4. What is the longest bone in the body?   *femur*

EXTENSION:

X rays can be obtained from a local hospital and used by the students to identify bones. Discuss how different types of joints allow certain types of movement in all directions. The knee joint allows movement in one direction. The lower jaw allows only partial movement.

ACTIVITY 2-3: Matter in Bone (page 30)

OBJECTIVE: To determine the approximate percentage of water and mineral content of bone.

CLASS TIME ALLOTMENT: 10 minutes on each of two days, plus oven time.

MATERIALS:

beef bone
balance
oven

PREPARATION NOTES:

In this activity the student measures the loss of water from a bone that occurs when the bone is heated. This activity may be done at home. Check with the home economics department for possible use of an oven to heat the bone if this activity is done in class. The percent of water in the bone may be calculated by this equation:

$$\frac{\text{weight of fresh bone} - \text{weight of dried bone}}{\text{weight of fresh bone}} \times 100$$

PROCEDURE:

1. Obtain a fresh beef bone.
2. Measure and record the mass of the bone. Describe the bone's appearance—hard, spongy, and so on.
3. Heat the bone in an oven at 65°C for 3 h. Allow the bone to cool.
4. Measure and record the bone's mass again.

OBSERVATIONS AND DATA:

A	B	C	D	E
Mass of bone before heating	Mass of bone after heating	Loss in mass	Percentage of mineral in bone	Percentage of water in bone

The bone lost mass upon heating. This mass loss is due primarily to water loss. A bone can be expected to contain 15-45% water. Mineral content may range from 55-85% of a bone's mass.

QUESTIONS AND CONCLUSIONS:

Bone, although it appears to be solid, is composed of cellular material that in turn contains considerable water. If bone is composed of water and minerals, mass of minerals can be calculated by removing the water. Calcium and phosphorus are the two main minerals in bone.
1. What happened to the mass of the bone?   *It decreased.*
2. What material was lost from the bone?   *liquids such as water*
3. What material was left?   *minerals such as calcium and phosphorous*
4. What percentage of the bone's mass was mineral matter? *Answers may vary.*

ADDITIONAL QUESTIONS:

5. What percentage of the bone's mass was water?   *Answers may vary.*
6. (a) What was lost from the bone during heating?   *water*
   (b) Why?   *Water begins to evaporate at about 65°C in the oven.*
7. Why were minerals not lost from the bone during heating?   *Minerals can not be evaporated when using such low temperatures.*
8. (a) What type of results would be obtained if the bone used was not fresh?
   inaccurate results
   (b) Why?   *Much of the water may have been already lost from it.*

ADDITIONAL ACTIVITY: Can You Stop Your Eyes From Blinking? (section 2:5)

OBJECTIVE: To show that some muscles are both voluntary and involuntary

CLASS TIME ALLOTMENT: 15 minutes.

MATERIALS:

classroom clock (or watch)

PREPARATION NOTES:

Students should work in pairs so one can watch the other for involuntary blinking. Teacher can call out seconds if classroom clock with second hand is unavailable.

PROCEDURE:

1. Blink your eyelids. NOTE: Point out to students that blinking is an example of voluntary control.
2. Determine how long you can keep from blinking. Time should be recorded on paper so that student data may be compared.
3. Repeat the experiment several times and take an average time.
NOTE: Point out to students that blinking under these conditions was involuntary.

OBSERVATIONS AND DATA:

Students should find an average time for not blinking from at least three trials. Students discover that they can control this for only about 10-20 seconds. The automatic blinking response will occur even though we are consciously telling it not to.

QUESTIONS AND CONCLUSIONS:

Blinking of the eye is usually an involuntary muscle action. We do not have to think about it; it occurs automatically. Under certain conditions we, can, however, voluntarily control this process by simply telling ourselves that we wish to blink. We can do the opposite also. We can tell ourselves to stop blinking.

1. Is blinking three times a voluntary or involuntary action?   *voluntary*
2. Is the normal blinking of eyes voluntary or involuntary?   *involuntary*
3. Is the stopping of blinking voluntary or involuntary?   *voluntary*
4. (a) Can you stop blinking for a very long time?   *no*
   (b) What does this tell you about the ability to control involuntary actions for long periods of time?   *One cannot do this. The involuntary action will take over.*
5. (a) Is coughing voluntary or involuntary?   *both*
   (b) Can you stop coughing if you tell yourself that you don't want to cough?   *maybe, for only a short time, then you will cough*
6. Why is blinking necessary?   *to keep the eye moist, and to protect the eye*

CHALLENGE: APPLYING SCIENTIFIC METHODS
Beets and Diffusion

OBJECTIVE: To observe diffusion into and out of cells

CLASS TIME ALLOTMENT:
30 minutes.

MATERIALS:

beets, fresh	test tube rack	knife
chemical A (HCl)	test tubes, 3	metric ruler
chemical B (NaOH)	water	watch or clock
marking pencil	graduated cylinder	

PREPARATION NOTES:

In this activity students place small chunks of beet into test tubes containing different chemicals and observe any color changes that occur. Prepare the HCl by slowly adding 8.6 mL of concentrated HCl to 1.0 L distilled water. Prepare NaOH by dissolving 4.0 g of sodium hydroxide in 1.0 L of distilled water. Caution students that the chemicals are harmful to skin and clothing. If spillage occurs, have students rinse immediately with water.

PROCEDURE:

1. Label three tubes A, B, and C. Fill these tubes with the following:
   Tube A: 5 mL chemical A (an acid)
   Tube B: 5 mL chemical B (a base)
   Tube C: 5 mL water
2. Slice a piece of beet into 3 small chunks of equal size. Each chunk should be no larger than about 3 mm on each side. Record the color of each beet cube.
3. Place one beet cube in each tube. Wait 15 minutes.
4. After waiting, look for any color change along the edges of each beet cube. Compare each cube color to the beet in tube C.
5. Record the color changes observed.

OBSERVATIONS AND DATA:

Students should note a color change in tubes A and B. The beet in tube A should change from red to deep red. The beet in tube B should change from red to yellow. You may want to have students record their data in a table similar to the one below.

TUBE	COLOR AT START	COLOR AFTER
A	red	deep red
B	red	yellow
C	red	red

QUESTIONS AND CONCLUSIONS:

1. (a) At the start of the experiment, what was the color of all three beet cubes?   *red*
   (b) At the end of the experiment, what was the color of the beet cubes in Tube A? Tube B? Tube C?   *A: deep red, B: yellow, C: red*
2. Were chemicals A and B present on the inside of beet cells at the start of the experiment?   *no*

3. (a)Were chemicals A and B present on the inside of the beet cells at the end of the experiment?   *yes*
   (b) What is your proof?   *Color changes occurred inside the beet cells.*
4. How did chemicals A and B get there?   *The chemicals moved into the cells by passing through cell membranes.*
5. What name is used to describe this process?   *The process is diffusion.*
6. (a) If you had used living celery cells instead of beet, would chemicals A and B have moved into the celery cells?   *yes*
   (b) Could you prove that A and B moved into celery cells if no color changes were observed?   *no*
   (c) Why are beet cells ideal for this kind of experiment?   *The red color inside the beet cells changes when acids or bases come in contact with it. This change is easily observed.*

---

chapter 3

Circulatory Systems

ACTIVITY 3-1: Blood Clotting (page 40)

OBJECTIVE: To determine the time needed for blood to clot

CLASS TIME ALLOTMENT: 20 minutes.

MATERIALS:

blood
dropper
microscope slide

needle
clock or watch with second hand

PREPARATION NOTES:

In this activity students observe the clotting of blood, and the time it takes for a clot to form. The slide must be clean. Dirt will interfere with the clotting process.

PROCEDURE:

Place a drop of blood on a microscope slide. Draw a needle through the blood every half minute. When solid material begins to cling to the needle, clotting has begun.

OBSERVATIONS AND DATA:

Normal clotting time is between 6 and 10 minutes.

QUESTIONS AND CONCLUSIONS:

1. How long does it take for clotting to begin?   *Answers will vary. 6-10 minutes*

ADDITIONAL QUESTIONS:

2. What might happen to a person with a slow clotting time?   *They could lose more blood from a minor cut or injury than a person with normal blood clotting time.*

ADDITIONAL ACTIVITY: Blood Cells (section 3:2)

OBJECTIVE: To observe the kinds of cells in the blood

CLASS TIME ALLOTMENT: 30 minutes.

MATERIALS:

microscope   prepared slide of human blood

PREPARATION NOTES:

Explain to students that each type of blood cell has its own recognizable characteristics. Red blood cells are round and are flat in the middle. White blood cells are round and have nuclei. Platelets are cell-like structures about ¼ the size of red blood cells.

PROCEDURE:

1. Examine a prepared slide of human blood under low power and high power.
2. Observe the red blood cells.
3. Draw a red blood cell and label the cell membrane and cytoplasm.
4. Move the slide slowly until you locate blood cells that have different shapes. These are white blood cells.
5. Draw a white blood cell and label the cell parts.
6. Slowly move the slide until you see very small dotlike platelets. Draw and label one or two platelets.

OBSERVATIONS AND DATA:

Students should observe and draw the following:

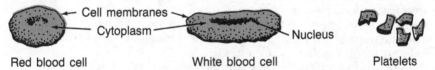

Red blood cell   White blood cell   Platelets

FIGURE 3-1

QUESTIONS AND CONCLUSIONS:

1. Describe the shape of a red blood cell.   *round*
2. Does a red blood cell have a nucleus?   *no*
3. Which blood cells were the most numerous on the slide?   *red blood cells*
4. Do the white blood cells have a nucleus?   *yes*

ADDITIONAL ACTIVITY: Blood Movement in Goldfish Capillaries (section 3:3)

OBJECTIVE: To observe the flow of blood in a living animal

CLASS TIME ALLOTMENT: 25 minutes.

MATERIALS:

cheesecloth or cotton   glass slide   microscope   water
glass plate, 5 × 10 cm   goldfish or guppy   tape

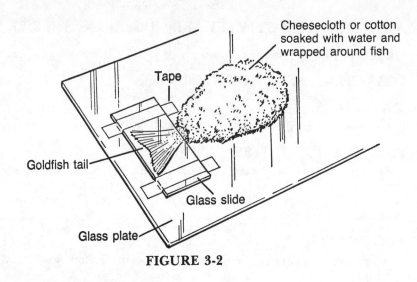

Cheesecloth or cotton soaked with water and wrapped around fish

Tape

Goldfish tail

Glass slide

Glass plate

FIGURE 3-2

PREPARATION NOTES:

CAUTION: Keep the goldfish moist at all times. Add water to the cheesecloth every few minutes and keep the fish under the microscope for only a short time.

PROCEDURE:

1. Wrap a goldfish in wet cheesecloth. Make sure that its tail is sticking out of the cheesecloth wrap. Moisten the cheesecloth.
2. Place the animal on a glass plate. Place a microscope glass slide over its tail and secure loosely with tape.
3. Position the glass plate on a microscope stage so that the fish tail appears over the stage opening. Use only low power magnification to observe the tail and blood capillaries present.
4. Remind students to add water to the cheesecloth every few minutes. Keep the fish under the microscope for only a short time (no longer than 10 minutes) and then return it to its original container. Observe the direction of blood flow in a specific capillary. Observe the speed of blood flow in a specific capillary. Look for differences in speed of blood flow in a specific capillary.

OBSERVATIONS AND DATA:

Students should be able to see small blood capillaries and blood cells flowing through these capillaries. The direction of blood flow should only be one way for a specific capillary.

QUESTIONS AND CONCLUSIONS:

1 What name is given to the small blood vessels seen in a fish tail?   *capillaries*
2. Does blood change its direction of flow in one small vessel?   *no*
3. Is the speed of blood movement rapid or slow?   *rapid*
4. (a) Does the speed of blood movement in a blood vessel seem to change?   *yes*
   (b) What may account for this?   *the pumping action of the heart*

5. Blood moves through some small capillaries one cell at a time. Why might this be helpful? *The cells moving through one at a time are able to drop off chemicals needed by cells and pick up waste materials easily.*

ACTIVITY 3-2: Heartbeat Rate: The Pulse Rate (page 44)

OBJECTIVE: To take a pulse and to compare pulse rates

CLASS TIME ALLOTMENT: 15 minutes.

MATERIALS: clock or watch with second hand

PREPARATION NOTES:

In this activity the student learns to detect a pulse and to measure the pulse rate. Have students do this activity when resting. Then have them do some jumping jacks and measure the pulse rate after the exercise. Discuss the difference in the pulse rate before and after exercise.

PROCEDURE:

1. Place the tips of your index and middle fingers gently on one side of your neck. Place the fingers below the jawbone and halfway between the main neck muscles and the windpipe. Locate a throbbing inside your neck.

FIGURE 3-3

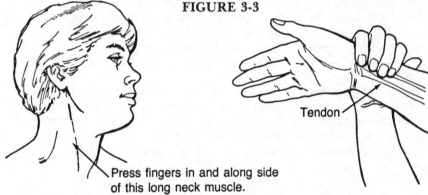

Tendon

Press fingers in and along side of this long neck muscle.

2. Count the number of throbs you feel in 10 seconds. Record this number.
3. Multiply the number by 6 and record it. This is your pulse rate—the number of throbs or beats in one minute.
4. Repeat Steps 1-3 two more times.
5. Determine your average pulse rate by adding the three pulse rates and dividing the sum by 3.
6. Record the average pulse rate for each member of your class.

OBSERVATIONS AND DATA:

	PULSE RATE
Trial 1.	
Trial 2.	
Trial 3.	
Average of trials	
Class average	

Normal pulse rate 1 minute _____
Pulse rate after walking up stairs_____
Pulse rate after running in place_____

Student pulse rates will vary. They should, however, fall within a range of 60-110 beats per minute. Students may observe changes in pulse rate from one trial to the next. When doing exercise, students should note that their pulse rate increases. The more strenuous the exercise, the higher the rate. Therefore, running in place should show a higher pulse rate when compared to walking up stairs.

QUESTIONS AND CONCLUSIONS:

1. What is the highest rate in your class? What is the lowest rate? *Answers will vary.*
2. What is the average pulse rate for your class? *Average resting pulse rate for 12-14 year olds is 72.*
3. How do you think your pulse rate would be affected by exercise? *Exercise increases heartbeat.* Devise an activity to test your hypothesis. *Compare pulse rate of student at rest with rate after student runs in place for two or three minutes.*

ADDITIONAL QUESTIONS:

4. (a) What is your average pulse rate for 1 minute? *will vary*
   (b) Are all student pulse rates in your class the same? *no*
5. Why is it best to repeat taking your pulse three times rather than only doing it once? *If a mistake is made, three trials will cancel any error.*
6. (a) Does your pulse remain the same while exercising? *no*
   (b) Does it go up or down when compared to your normal pulse? *goes up*
7. Choose the statement which seems best. *answer c*
   (a) As exercise becomes more difficult, pulse rate does not change.
   (b) As exercise becomes more difficult, pulse rate gets slower.
   (c) As exercise becomes more difficult, pulse rate gets faster.
8. How is your pulse rate related to your heartbeat? *They are exactly the same.*

ACTIVITY 3-3: The Heartbeat (page 47)

OBJECTIVE: To determine what the heartbeat sounds like when using a stethoscope

CLASS TIME ALLOTMENT: 10 minutes.

MATERIALS:

stethoscope (NOTE: To construct a stethoscope if one is not available, you need the following items: small plastic funnel; glass or plastic Y tube; rubber or plastic tube lengths 24-30 cm (2); rubber or plastic tube lengths 5 cm.)

PREPARATION NOTES:

In this activity students use a stethoscope to listen to a person's heartbeat. Heartbeat is usually faster in young children than in adults. Point out to students that the lub-dub sound of the heart is caused by the opening and closing of the heart valves. A physician is trained to detect abnormalities of the heart from the sound of the heartbeat.

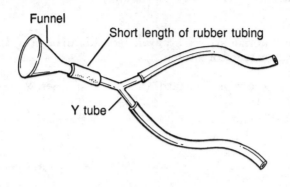

Funnel

Short length of rubber tubing

Y tube

FIGURE 3-4

PROCEDURE:

Listen to a person's heartbeat with a stethoscope.

OBSERVATIONS AND DATA:

Heart sounds are described as being a "lub-dub" sound. The first or "lub" sound is the loudest and is caused by the closing of the valves located between the atria and ventricles. The second or "dub" sound is quieter and is caused by closing of semilunar valves located in the aorta and pulmonary artery. NOTE: It will be very difficult for students to detect differences or abnormal sounds in other students. They may, however, be able to detect different rates.

QUESTIONS AND CONCLUSIONS:

1. What sounds do you hear repeated over and over again in perfect rhythm? *lub-dub; sounds differ*
2. Listen to the heartbeats of several people of different ages. How are the sounds similar and different? *Younger people generally have faster heartbeats. Answers will vary.*

ADDITIONAL QUESTIONS:

3. What is the value of a stethoscope? *to magnify sound*
4. Choose what best describes the heart sounds you hear. *(c) lub-dub*
   (a) bump-blip (b) blip-blip (c) lub-dub (d) dub-lub
5. There are two heart sounds. Which one is loudest? *the first*
6. (a) What can be heard after each heart sound? *nothing*
   (b) What may be happening to the heart at this time? *resting*
7. What causes heart sounds? *closing of heart valves*

ADDITIONAL ACTIVITY: Effect of Hardness on Pressure (section 3:9)

OBJECTIVE: To compare the pressure found in rigid tubing (artery) to that in flexible tubing (vein).

CLASS TIME ALLOTMENT: 30 minutes.

MATERIALS:

(NOTE: These materials are readily available and can be provided for each student or team of students.)

basin optional
bottle, plastic squeeze type (mustard, catsup)
glass tubing—20 cm
glass tubing—3 cm
meter stick

rubber tubing—18 cm
stopper, 2-hole, to fit bottle
water

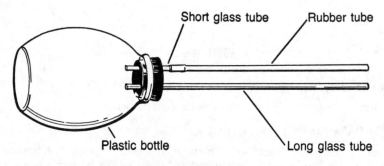

Short glass tube   Rubber tube

Plastic bottle   Long glass tube

FIGURE 3-5

PREPARATION NOTES:

You may wish to prepare stopper assemblies before class. Insert the long glass tube into one hole of the two-hole stopper. Insert the short glass tube into the other hole. Attach the rubber tube to the short glass tube so that the long glass tube and the rubber tube are the same length as shown in Figure 3-5.

PROCEDURE:

1. Fill the plastic bottle with water. Replace the stopper.
2. Position the bottle and a meter stick next to a sink (or large basin) as shown.

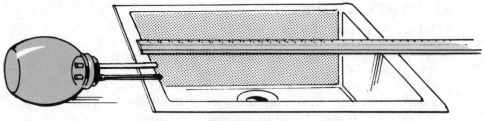

FIGURE 3-6

3. Have one student give the plastic bottle a moderate but very short squeeze. The water streaming out of both tubes will land in the sink at different distances from the ends of the tubes.
4. Measure the distance from the edge of the sink (in cm) to where the streams of water land (not the height from top to bottom of sink).

5. Record measurements in the table.
6. Repeat the squeezing and measuring three more times. Make sure that the bottle is refilled with water each time, and the pressure exerted and time spent squeezing the bottle are almost the same each time.
7. Calculate an average distance that the water spurts out for the glass tube and rubber tube.

OBSERVATIONS AND DATA:

DISTANCE TRAVELED BY WATER IN CENTIMETERS		
TRIALS	GLASS	RUBBER
1		
2		
3		
4		
totals		
averages		

The water stream will always spurt farther from the glass than from the rubber tube. The difference should be from 3-8 cm.

QUESTIONS AND CONCLUSIONS:

The plastic squeeze bottle represents the heart. Water represents blood, while the glass tube represents an artery. Rubber tubing represents a vein. Arteries are rigid and therefore contain blood under high pressure. Veins are flexible and contain blood under low pressure.
1. Comparing the squeeze bottle to an organ in the human body, what would the organ be?   *the heart*
2. Arteries are rigid (do not give easily) while veins are soft and flexible (do give).
   (a) Which material, glass or rubber, was supposed to be an artery?   *glass*
   (b) Which material, glass or rubber, was supposed to be a vein?   *rubber*
3. Which material, glass or rubber, had the stream of water that went the farthest?   *glass*
4. Arteries have blood under high pressure. Blood could spurt from an artery for a greater distance than could blood from a vein. Do your results agree with this?   *yes*

CHALLENGE: APPLYING SCIENTIFIC METHODS
A Close Look at a Sheep Heart

OBJECTIVE: To examine the main parts of a sheep heart and to trace the pathway of blood through the heart.

CLASS TIME ALLOTMENT: One period.

MATERIALS:
dissecting pan or paper toweling
dissecting tools
sheep heart

PREPARATION NOTES:

In this activity students examine the inside and outside of a sheep heart and locate certain main parts. Sheep hearts are available from biological supply houses or may be obtained from a local butcher or slaughter house. The following diagrams are provided for your reference.

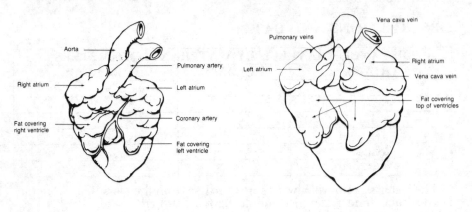

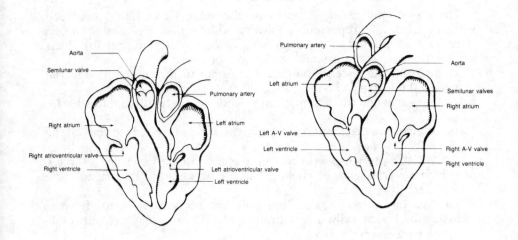

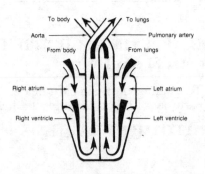

FIGURE 3-7

PROCEDURE:

1. Position your sheep heart on the dissecting pan so that the aorta is on the bottom and the pulmonary artery is on the top. NOTE: As the heart lies in this position, the right side of the heart is on your left. The left side of the heart is on your right.
2. Identify the parts of the heart using the information in the table.

Coronary artery	a small blood vessel found on front of heart, runs on an angle across heart
Left ventricle Right ventricle	the largest parts of heart, divided into left and right sides by coronary artery
Left atrium Right atrium	small ear or flaplike parts on top of each ventricle, only about ⅓ size of ventricles (Don't confuse with fat which may be just below each atrium.)
Pulmonary artery	large blood vessel which connects to top or right ventricle. This artery is in front at top of heart. Usually this artery is pointing on an angle.
Aorta	large blood vessel directly in back of pulmonary artery. It connects to top left ventricle. These two blood vessels crisscross at top of heart.
Vena cava veins	two large veins which enter the top and side of the right atrium. Usually the veins are missing and all that can be seen are the openings where they joined the atrium.
Pulmonary veins	two veins which enter the sides of the left atrium. Usually the veins are missing and all that can be seen is one opening where they joined the atrium.

3. Turn the heart over and locate the pulmonary and vena cava veins. NOTE: The left and right sides of the heart are no longer reversed.
4. Have your teacher slice the heart open into a front and back section. Replace both halves together and position the heart on your dissecting pan as you did in Step 1.
5. Remove the top half of the heart and put it aside. Use only the bottom for this part of the experiment. NOTE: Left and right sides are again reversed.
6. Identify the inside parts of the sheep heart.
7. Now examine the inside of the other half of your sheep heart. Identify the left ventricle, left atrium, aorta, pulmonary artery, and valves. NOTE: Atrioventricular (A-V) valves control the openings between the atria and ventricles. Semilunar valves control the flow of blood from the ventricles into the arteries. Depending on how your sheep heart was cut, not all parts listed above may show on your sheep heart half.
8. Examine the front half of your sheep heart again. Try to trace the pathway that blood follows through the heart. NOTE: Blood does not go directly from the heart's right side to the left side. It must go first to the lungs from the heart's right side and then back to the heart's left side. The

path of blood circulation is as follows: from body, right atrium, right ventricle, pulmonary artery to lungs, pulmonary vein from lungs to left atrium, left ventricle, aorta to body.

OBSERVATIONS AND DATA:

Students should observe all major parts of a sheep heart. You may wish to have students diagram their sheep hearts and label the major parts discussed in this activity.

QUESTIONS AND CONCLUSIONS:

1. What are the largest parts of the heart?   *The left and right ventricles are the largest parts of the heart.*
2. What two chambers or heart parts are located on top of the left and right ventricles?   *The left and right atria are located on top of the left and right ventricles.*
3. What blood vessel is found on the outside of the heart ventricles?   *The coronary artery*
4. (a) Which valves separate blood between atria and ventricles? *The atrioventricular (A-V) valves separate the blood between the atria and ventricles.*
   (b) Which valves are found inside the aorta (and pulmonary artery)?   *The semilunar valves are found inside the aorta.*
5. (a) Which ventricle of the heart has the thickest muscles?   *The left ventricle has the thickest muscles.*
   (b) Offer a reason why this may be important.   *The left ventricle must pump blood to the entire body.*
6. Blood flow through the heart always follows a certain pattern. Complete each of the following sentences.
   (a) Blood arrives at the right atrium from the   *body.*
   (b) Blood arrives at the left atrium from the   *lungs.*
   (c) Blood is pumped from right atrium directly to   *the right ventricle.*
   (d) Blood is pumped from left atrium directly to   *the left ventricle.*
   (e) Blood flows to the lungs along the   *pulmonary artery.*
   (f) Blood flows to the body along the   *aorta.*

---

chapter 4

Internal Body Processes

ADDITIONAL ACTIVITY: A Test for Carbon Dioxide (section 4:2)

OBJECTIVE: To determine if carbon dioxide gas is present in exhaled air

CLASS TIME ALLOTMENT: 20 minutes.

MATERIALS: beaker or glass jar, 100 mL   straw
limewater

PREPARATION NOTES:

To prepare limewater, add calcium hydroxide in excess to 1000 mL distilled water. Allow to remain overnight. Filter and store clear liquid (limewater) in an airtight container.

PROCEDURE:

1. Add 50 mL of limewater to a beaker. Observe and record the color of the limewater.
2. Exhale through a straw and bubble your breath through the limewater. Do this for at least 2 minutes.
3. Observe and record the color of the limewater now.

OBSERVATIONS AND DATA:

Limewater changes from its clear color to a milky white.

QUESTIONS AND CONCLUSIONS:

The change from clear to milky white is an indication that exhaled air does contain carbon dioxide. The milky substance is calcium carbonate (limestone composition). It results from carbon dioxide reacting with the calcium hydroxide.

$$Ca(OH)_2 \quad + \quad CO_2 \longrightarrow CaCO_3 \quad + \ H_2O$$

calcium hydroxide + carbon dioxide $\longrightarrow$ calcium carbonate + water

1. What was the color of limewater before exhaling into it?   *clear*
2. What was the color of limewater after exhaling into it?   *milky white*
3. Carbon dioxide gas causes limewater to turn from colorless or clear to milky white. What gas is given off when you breathe out?   *carbon dioxide*

ACTIVITY 4-1: Rate of Breathing (page 62)

OBJECTIVE: To determine normal breathing rate and breathing rate after exercise

CLASS TIME ALLOTMENT: 20 minutes.

MATERIALS:

clock or watch with second hand

PREPARATION NOTES:

In this activity the student measures the rate of breathing and compares the rate before and after exercise. Stress the importance of students being absolutely quiet when making the first measurement. Caution students to exercise restraint when running in place, to immediately sit down, and to measure their breathing rates as soon as they are finished running.

PROCEDURE:

1. Sit quietly and count the number of breaths you take in 1 minute. Use a watch with a second hand.
2. Repeat step 1 two more times.
3. Calculate the average number of breaths you take per minute. Compare your rate of breathing with the rates of your classmates.

4. Run in place for 2 minutes.
5. Immediately determine your breathing rate as you did in Step 1.
6. Repeat Steps 4 and 5 two more times and calculate an average.

OBSERVATIONS AND DATA:

TRIALS	NUMBER OF BREATHS IN ONE MINUTE	
	NORMAL	AFTER EXERCISE
1		
2		
3		
Total		
Average		

Breathing rate under normal conditions should be about 14-18 times per minute. Breathing rate will increase following exercise.

QUESTIONS AND CONCLUSIONS:

1. How did your breathing rate change when you exercised?   *it goes up*
2. How would your breathing rate after swimming 10 min compare to the rate after walking 10 min? Explain your answer.   *Answers will vary. Rate will increase for both, but would be higher for strenuous swimming.*

ADDITIONAL QUESTIONS:

3. What is your average normal breathing rate for one minute?   *will vary*
4. (a) Which is more accurate, results from each trial or your average results?   *average*
   (b) Why?   *Averaging lessens the significance of errors in each trial.*
5. Why does your breathing rate increase after exercising?   *The demand for oxygen by the body is greater.*
6. Do you normally control your breathing rate or does it take place automatically?   *It is automatic (except when you decide to hold your breath).*

ACTIVITY 4-2: A Plant Enzyme (page 64)

OBJECTIVE: To observe the effects of an enzyme

CLASS TIME ALLOTMENT: One period.

MATERIALS:

barley seed-water mixture   graduated cylinder   test tubes, 6
burner   iodine solution   stoppers, 6
beakers, 100 mL, 2   marking pencil   test tube clamp
filter paper   spoon   test tube rack
funnel   starch solution

PREPARATION NOTES:

In this activity the student investigates the effects of an enzyme on starch. Show students how to fold a piece of filter paper before putting it into the funnel. Remind students to mark the test tubes carefully so they do not get mixed up. Have students draw a data table in their notebooks before they begin work. Demonstrate the proper procedure for boiling liquid in a test tube, and remind students not to point a test tube towards anyone when heating it. See Preparation of Solutions in Teacher's Guide for preparing starch.

PROCEDURE:
Part A
1. Filter a barley seed-water mixture by pouring it through a funnel lined with filter paper. Save the milky liquid. It contains the enzyme diastase. Dispose of the crushed seeds in a trash container.
2. Label 5 test tubes A, B, C, D, and E. Place them in the test tube rack.
3. Add 1 mL of the milky solution to each test tube. Save the rest of the milky solution for Part B.
4. Add 1 mL of starch solution to each test tube. Put a stopper in each tube and mix by inverting several times.
5. Add 3 drops of iodine solution to tube A. Mix by inverting. Record the color in your data table. If starch is present, the iodine will change color to blue-black.
6. Wait 5 min, then add 3 drops of iodine solution to tube B. Mix, observe, and record any color change.
7. Continue to add iodine to the remaining test tubes at 5 min intervals. Mix, observe, and record any color changes.
8. Empty and rinse the test tubes.

Part B
1. Pour the remaining diastase liquid into a test tube. Boil the liquid gently for 2 min. **CAUTION:** do not overheat or the liquid will boil out of the test tube.
2. Relabel the five test tubes F, G, H, I, and J. Place them in the test tube rack.
3. Add 1 mL of the boiled liquid and 1 mL of starch solution to each test tube. Add stoppers and mix each test tube.
4. Repeat Steps 6-8 of Part A. Record any color changes.

OBSERVATIONS AND DATA:

TEST TUBE	MATERIALS ADDED	RESULTS	STARCH PRESENT	
			YES	NO
A				

QUESTIONS AND CONCLUSIONS:
1. What happened when you added the iodine solution to test tube A?   *The solution turns blue-black.*
2. Was starch present in tube A? How do you know?   *Yes, the color change to blue-black indicates the presence of starch.*
3. Did all of the test tubes that contained starch have the same amount of starch? Explain.   *No, there appears to be decreasing amounts of starch as the enzyme has more time to act on the starch.*

4. What happened when you added the iodine to test tube F? *There was no color change.*
5. What is the function of the enzyme diastase? *It changes starch to another substance.*
6. How did boiling affect the action of diastase? *Boiling destroys the diastase so that it does not act on starch.*

ACTIVITY 4-3: Protein Digestion (page 67)

OBJECTIVE: To determine which chemicals can best bring about protein digestion

CLASS TIME ALLOTMENT: 20 minutes on each of two consecutive days.

MATERIALS:

egg white, hard-boiled	marking pencil	pepsin solution
knife	graduated cylinder	hydrochloric acid
test tubes, 4	water	test tube rack

PREPARATION NOTES:

In this activity the student investigates the effect of pepsin in digesting protein. Hard boil the egg before class so it is cooled to room temperature before use. The test tubes are kept in a warm place to simulate the temperature of the human body, about 37°C. See Preparation of Solutions in Teacher's Guide for preparation of pepsin and hydrochloric acid. Compare the action of the pepsin with hydrochloric acid to the acid state of the stomach. Remind students that the digestion of protein is a chemical change in which protein is changed to amino acids.

PROCEDURE:

1. Separate the white from a hard-boiled egg. Dispose of the rest of the egg.
2. Cut the egg white into four 1 cm cubes.
3. Label four test tubes A, B, C, and D. Add one cube of egg white to each tube.
4. Add the following to the test tubes as indicated.
   A—10 mL water
   B—10 mL pepsin solution
   C—10 mL hydrochloric acid
   D—10 mL pepsin solution and 2 drops dilute hydrochloric acid
5. Place the test tubes in a very warm place and leave them overnight.
6. Observe the test tubes.

OBSERVATIONS AND DATA:

Look for changes occurring along egg cube edges. Clear or fuzzy areas are to be construed as evidence of protein digestion. Record observations in a chart similar to the following and be especially alert to slight differences in each tube. Decide and indicate which tube or tubes show the greatest and least amount of digestion. Use the last column of chart to indicate this by ranking 1-4 (1—most digestion, 4—least digestion).

TUBE	CHEMICALS PRESENT	APPEARANCE OF EGG CUBE	AMOUNT OF DIGESTION
A			
B			
C			
D			

QUESTIONS AND CONCLUSIONS:

The tube showing the clearest edges will be tube D. Some clear or fuzzy edges may be noted in tubes B and C also but not to the extent of tube D. Tube A should show no digestion.

Protein (egg white) is digested best where both an acid and pepsin (an enzyme) are present. Tube D represents conditions found in the human stomach where protein digestion begins. Enzyme only (Tube B) or acid only (Tube C) may cause some digestion.

1. Why were the test tubes left in a warm place?   *warmth speeds chemical reactions*
2. In which test tubes did digestion occur?   *protein was digested in test tube D* How do you know?   *the egg was fuzzy around the edges*
3. What chemicals were present in the test tubes in which protein was digested?   *pepsin solution and dilute HC1*

ADDITIONAL QUESTIONS:

4. What did the egg white supply in the experiment?   *protein*
5. Which tubes showed the least protein digestion?   *tubes B and C*
6. Which tubes showed no protein digestion?   *tube A*
7. Why was it necessary to wait 24 hours?   *to allow the enzyme to digest protein*
8. What is pepsin?   *an enzyme that digests protein*

ACTIVITY 4-4: Starch Digestion (page 68)

OBJECTIVE: To observe if chewing a cracker will change it from starch to sugar

CLASS TIME ALLOTMENT: One period.

MATERIALS:

test tubes (3)   iodine solution   beaker
marking pencil   dropper   hot plate
soda cracker   Benedict's solution   clock or watch
water   graduated cylinder

PREPARATION NOTES:

In this activity students study the digestion of starch in the mouth. Review the sequence of procedures for this activity before students begin work. See Preparation of Solutions in Teacher's Guide for preparation of iodine and Benedict's solutions. Remind students of the safety precautions necessary when heating a test tube.

PROCEDURE:

1. Label 3 test tubes A, B, and C. Crumble a soda cracker and put ¼ of it in test tube A.
2. Add 3 mL of water. Mix by rotating the test tube between the palms of your hands.
3. Add 3 or 4 drops of iodine solution. Observe the result.
4. Put ¼ of the cracker into test tube B.
5. Add 5mL of Benedict's solution to the test tube.
6. Place the test tube in a beaker half full of water.
7. Chew a cracker for 1 min.
8. Place the chewed cracker in test tube C. Add 5 mL of Benedict's solution.
9. Place the test tube in the beaker with test tube B. Heat the water in the beaker for 5 min. If sugar is present, the color will change from green to orange.

OBSERVATIONS AND DATA:

	COLOR WITH IODINE	CONCLUSION	COLOR WITH BENEDICT'S SOLUTION	CONCLUSION
Cracker				
Chewed cracker				

Unchewed cracker with iodine turns blue. Unchewed cracker with Benedict's solution after heating remains blue. Chewed cracker with iodine does not change color. Chewed cracker with Benedict's solution after heating turns red, yellow, or orange.

QUESTIONS AND CONCLUSIONS:

Starch is present in the unchewed cracker. Evidence is obtained from the iodine and Benedict's tests performed on it. The chewed cracker now has sugar present. Evidence is from the iodine and Benedict's tests again. The starch in the cracker has been changed to sugar by the action of a chemical present in the mouth. This chemical is saliva and it contains a starch-digesting enzyme called ptyalin.

1. Did the cracker in test tube A contain starch? How do you know?   *Yes, there was a color change when the iodine solution was added.*
2. Did the unchewed cracker contain sugar?   *no*
3. Did the chewed cracker contain sugar?   *yes* How did you tell?   *The color change shows that starch in the chewed cracker was changed to sugar by saliva.*
4. What happened to the starch in the chewed cracker?   *It was changed to sugar by saliva.*

ADDITIONAL QUESTIONS:

5. (a) Does a cracker contain starch or sugar?   *starch*
   (b) What is your evidence?   *iodine test turned blue; Benedict's test stayed blue after heating.*
6. (a) Does a chewed cracker contain starch or sugar?   *sugar*
   (b) What is your evidence? *Benedict's test turned red (yellow) after heating*

7. What did the chewing of a cracker have to do with the experiment? *It supplied a chemical that changed starch to sugar. (It was not physical chewing that caused the change.)*
8. What may be present in your mouth that can do this? *an enzyme*
9. Why is this an important step in digestion of foods? *starch foods must be changed to sugar in order for the body to use them as food; this change begins in the mouth*
10. How could you prove that it is not simply chewing of the cracker that causes it to change? *Place cracker in bowl. Add water and crush. Test with iodine and Benedict's. Starch will still be present.*

ACTIVITY 4-5: Fat Digestion (page 69)

OBJECTIVE: To determine if bile can aid the process of fat digestion

CLASS TIME ALLOTMENT: One period.

MATERIALS:

test tubes (3)	vegetable oil	bile solution
marking pencil	dropper	stoppers, solid (3)
graduated cylinder	baking soda	test tube rack
water	flat toothpick	clock or watch

PREPARATION NOTES:

In this activity students observe the effect of bile on fat. See Preparation of Solutions in Teacher's Guide for preparation of bile. Use within 24 hours. Bile emulsifies fat, which means it breaks it up into tiny particles, thereby increasing the surface area for digestion. Bile does not cause a chemical change in the fat.

PROCEDURE:

1. Label 3 test tubes A, B, and C. Add 10 mL water to each test tube.
2. Add 3 drops vegetable oil to each test tube.
3. Add a small amount of baking soda (the amount that stays on the wide end of a flat toothpick) to test tube B.
4. Add 5 drops bile solution to test tube C.
5. Stopper each test tube and mix the oil and water by inverting and shaking each tube several times.
6. Allow the test tubes to stand for 10 min.

OBSERVATIONS AND DATA:

TUBE	CHEMICALS ADDED	ORDER OF SEPARATION
A		
B		
C		

The tube with only oil and water (tube A) will show fat and water separation quickly (1-2 min of waiting). Tube B will show some separation after 4-5 min of waiting. Tube C will show no separation after 10 minutes.

QUESTIONS AND CONCLUSIONS:

Oil (fat) normally does not mix with water. However, if oil particles can be first broken up (emulsified) into small enough droplets, they will mix with water. This break up of fats is a necessary step in their digestion. When broken up, they can be easily digested by enzymes. Bile is normally produced in the human body and aids in breaking up fats. This was evident in tube C where no separation of oil and water occurred.

1. In which test tubes did the oil and water separate?   *A and B*
2. How did the baking soda affect the rate of separation?   *It slowed down the rate.*
3. How does bile affect the mixing of oil and water?   *It allows them to mix.*
4. Does bile cause a chemical change in fats?   *no, causes only a physical change*

ADDITIONAL QUESTIONS:

5. What is the reason for adding oil to each tube?   *oil is a fat*
6. (a) Which tube showed the fastest separation of oil and water after mixing?   *tube A*
   (b) What was added to this tube?   *oil and water*
7. (a) Which tube showed the slowest, or no separation of oil and water after mixing?   *tube C*
   (b) What was added to this tube?   *oil, water, and bile*
8. If oil drop size can be made small enough, it will not separate when mixed with water.
   (a) Which tube had the smallest sized oil drops after mixing?   *tube C*
   (b) What chemical aids in making oil drops small?   *bile*
9. (a) Which chemical, sodium bicarbonate or bile, is normally produced by the body?   *bile*
   (b) What is bile's function?   *to break up fat (oil) into smaller sized particles, thus helping to speed digestion of fats*

ACTIVITY 4-6: Diffusion and Absorption (page 70)

OBJECTIVE: To observe the diffusion of iodine through dialysis tubing

CLASS TIME ALLOTMENT: 20 minutes.

MATERIALS:

2 large jars or beakers	starch solution
iodine solution	graduated cylinder, 100 mL
dialysis tubing, 20 cm and 60 cm	water
string	clock or watch
knife	

PREPARATION NOTES:

In this activity students investigate the diffusion of iodine through dialysis tubing. Dialysis tubing is made of cellulose and is used to demonstrate diffusion. Packaged dialysis tubing has a water proof film on each surface that should be removed by soaking in 19% ethyl (grain) alcohol for about 3 minutes. Then rinse off the coating in water. See Preparation of Solutions in Teacher's Guide for preparation of starch and iodine. For best results, allow the jars to stand for a few hours.

PROCEDURE:

1. Fill 2 large empty jars with iodine solution.
2. Cut two lengths of dialysis tubing, one 20 cm and the other 60 cm.
3. Tie one end of each piece of tubing shut with pieces of string.
4. Pour 20 mL of starch solution into each piece of dialysis tubing. Tie remaining ends of the tubing closed.
5. Rinse the outside of each piece of dialysis tubing with water.
6. Put one piece of tubing containing the starch solution into each jar of iodine. Be sure the ends of the tubing are above the solution level.
7. Let the jars stand for 10 min. Observe and record the color of the starch solution in each jar.

OBSERVATIONS AND DATA:

The starch turns blue-black when it reacts with the iodine. The jar with the longer tubing has the darker color. This is because there is more surface area for diffusion of the iodine.

QUESTIONS AND CONCLUSIONS:

1. What happened to the color of the starch?   *starch turned blue-black*
2. What caused this change?   *Iodine diffused through the dialysis tubing and reacted with the starch.*
3. Was there a difference in the color of the starch in the two jars?   *jar with the longer tubing had darker color*
4. How do you account for this difference?   *more surface area for diffusion*
5. How is this activity similar to food absorption in the body?   *Because of the villi, the small intestine has a large surface area for food absorption.*
6. How would food absorption be affected if there were no villi in the small intestine?   *Food absorption would be much slower without villi.*

CHALLENGE: APPLYING SCIENTIFIC METHODS
Testing "Urine"

OBJECTIVE: To perform three different chemical tests on an imitation urine specimen

CLASS TIME ALLOTMENT: One period.

MATERIALS:

acid (HCl)
base (NaOH)
droppers
glass marking pencil
glucose testing tablets (Clinitest)
glucose water
litmus paper, red and blue
salt water

silver nitrate
test tube rack
test tubes
tweezers
urine sample
watch glass
water, distilled

PREPARATION NOTES:

In this activity the student learns how to perform three chemical tests and then performs these tests on an imitation urine sample. Caution students not to spill acid or base on hands or clothing. If spillage occurs, rinse immediately with water. Also, silver nitrate will stain skin and clothing.

Avoid contact with this chemical. To prepare HCl slowly add 8.6 mL concentrated HCl to 1.0 L distilled water. To prepare NaOH, dissolve 4.0 g NaOH in 1.0 L distilled water. To prepare silver nitrate, dissolve 1.0 g silver nitrate in 100 mL distilled water. "Urine" is distilled water with 1 or 2 drops of yellow food coloring added. Salt of glucose may be added. Glucose water can be made by adding 10 g glucose to 1.0 L distilled water. Salt water can be made by dissolving 20 g sodium chloride in 1.0 L distilled water. The Clinitest is available from drug stores. If you wish, a glass slide may be substituted for the watch glass.

PROCEDURE:

Part A. Doing the Glucose Test
1. Number 2 test tubes 1 and 2.
2. Place the following into each tube:
   Tube 1: 10 drops distilled water
   Tube 2: 10 drops glucose water
3. Place both tubes in a test tube rack. Using tweezers add a glucose testing tablet to each tube. **CAUTION:** Do not handle tablets with fingers.
4. Wait 2 minutes. Record the colors that appear in both tubes.

Part B. Doing the Salt Test
1. Number 2 clean test tubes A and B.
2. Place the following into each tube.
   Tube A: 10 drops distilled water
   Tube B: 10 drops salt water
3. Place both tubes in a test tube rack. Add two drops of silver nitrate to both tubes. Record the colors that appear in both tubes.

Part C. Doing the Acid or Base Test
1. Take a strip of red and blue litmus paper and cut each strip into thirds. Place the pieces on a watch glass.
2. Use one small piece of each of the litmus papers for the next step. Add 1 drop of distilled water to a piece of red and blue litmus paper. Record the color changes, if any. You now have a way of determining if a liquid is neither an acid nor a base.
3. Add a drop of acid to a piece of red and blue litmus paper. Record the color changes. You now have a way of determining if a liquid is an acid.
4. Add a drop of base to a piece of red and blue litmus paper. Record the color changes. You now have a way of determining if a liquid is a base.

Part D. Doing the Glucose, Salt, and Acid or Base Tests on Urine
1. Place 10 drops of urine into a test tube and place it in a test tube rack. Using tweezers, add a glucose testing tablet. Wait 2 minutes. Record the color that appears in the test tube.
2. Place 10 drops of urine in a clean test tube. Place the tube in a rack. Add 2 drops of silver nitrate. Record the color that appears in the tube.
3. Add 1 drop of urine to small pieces of red and blue litmus paper. Record the colors that appear on each paper.
4. Using your results from the three tests, determine if your urine sample is acid or base, if glucose is present, or if salt is present.

OBSERVATIONS AND DATA:

Part A: Glucose will make the tablet change color to green, yellow, orange, or red. If no glucose is present, the color will be blue.

Part B: Silver nitrate and salt form a white precipitate. No change occurs in the tube that has only water and silver nitrate.

Part C: Water causes no change in either color of litmus paper. Acids cause blue litmus to turn red. Acids will not change the color of red litmus. Bases cause red litmus to turn blue. Bases do not change the color of blue litmus.

Part D: Results will vary with the content of the "urine."

QUESTIONS AND CONCLUSIONS:

1. (a) What color appears in a tube if glucose is not present? *blue*
   (b) What color appears in a tube if glucose is present? *green, yellow, orange, or red*
   (c) What color appeared in the tube after doing the glucose test on urine? *Answers will vary.*
   (d) Was glucose present in the urine sample? *Answers will vary.*
2. (a) What color appears in a tube if salt is not present? *no color*
   (b) What color appears in a tube if salt is present? *A white haze (precipitate) appears.*
   (c) What color appeared in the tube after doing the salt test on urine? *Answers will vary.*
3. (a) What color appears on red and blue litmus paper if an acid is present? *Red litmus paper remains red, and blue litmus paper turns red.*
   (b) What color appears on red and blue litmus paper if a base is present? *Red litmus paper turns blue, and blue litmus paper remains blue.*
   (c) What colors appeared on red and blue litmus paper after doing the acid and base test on urine? *Answers will vary, but normally there should be no color change.*
   (d) Was an acid or base present in the sample? *Student answers will vary, but normally there will not be acids or bases in their sample.*

---

chapter 5

Nervous and Endocrine Systems

ACTIVITY 5-1: The Sense of Touch (page 84)

OBJECTIVE: To investigate the sense of touch at different areas of the body

CLASS TIME ALLOTMENT: 20 minutes.

MATERIALS:
large index card
metric ruler
2 round toothpicks

PREPARATION NOTES:

In this activity the student investigates the sense of touch. This activity can easily be done at home, and you may wish to make it a homework assignment.

PROCEDURE:

1. Use a toothpick to punch a small hole in the index card.
2. Use the ruler and toothpick to measure and punch holes 1 mm, 3 mm, 5 mm, and 10 mm from the first hole.
3. Insert the two toothpicks into the holes that are 1 mm apart. The ends of the toothpicks should be even.
4. Work with a partner. Have the person close his or her eyes. Gently touch the tips of the toothpicks to the skin surface of the fingertips, palm, back of neck, and above the elbow. Have your partner tell you how many toothpick tips are touching the skin in each area.
5. Repeat Step 4 with the toothpicks placed at 3 mm, 5 mm, and 10 mm. Record the results.

OBSERVATIONS AND DATA:

DISTANCE	NUMBER OF TOOTHPICKS FELT			
	FINGER-TIPS	PALM	BACK OF NECK	ABOVE THE ELBOW
1 mm				
3 mm				
5 mm				
10 mm				

QUESTIONS AND CONCLUSIONS:

1. Which skin area was most sensitive?   *fingertips; being able to detect points best on fingertips indicates more nerve endings*
2. Why are some areas of the body more sensitive to touch than other areas? *Some areas are more sensitive because receptors are closer together.*
3. In what way is touch important in preventing injury?   *Touch aids you in avoiding hot or sharp objects.*

ACTIVITY 5-2: Taste (page 85)

OBJECTIVE: To investigate the different tastes distinguished by the tongue

CLASS TIME ALLOTMENT: 20 minutes.

MATERIALS:

graduated cylinder	baking soda	marking pencil
water	salt	cotton swabs
beakers, 500 mL, 4	vinegar	cup
sugar	spoon	

PREPARATION NOTES:

In this activity, students investigate the sense of taste. Go over the procedure to be used in preparing and tasting the solutions. Caution students to follow sterile procedures. A cotton swab should be used for tasting a solution and then should immediately be thrown into a trash container. Each student should use a new swab for each taste. Be certain that beakers or glasses have been cleaned.

This activity can be easily done at home, and you may wish to make it a homework assignment.

PROCEDURE:

1. Working with a partner, prepare 4 solutions. Place 400 mL of water in each of 4 beakers. To the first beaker add 1 spoonful of sugar; to the second beaker add 1 spoonful of baking soda; to the third beaker add 1 spoonful of salt; and to the fourth beaker add 1 spoonful of vinegar.
2. Have your partner label the beakers and then move them around so you do not know which solution is in each beaker. Using a sterile cotton swab, dip into the first solution and run the swab over your tongue. Record the taste of the solution.
3. Discard the swab and rinse your mouth with water.
4. Using a new swab each time, repeat Steps 2 and 3 for the other solutions. Record your results.

OBSERVATIONS AND DATA:

BEAKER	TASTE OF SOLUTION
1	
2	
3	
4	

QUESTIONS AND CONCLUSIONS:

1. What taste sensations did you identify?   *Answers will vary. salty, sour, bitter, and sweet*
2. Did you have to taste any solution a second time in order to identify it? If so, which solution?   *Answers will vary.*
3. Hold your nose and try the taste tests again. Did you have any difficulty identifying the solutions this time? Why or why not?   *Answers will vary; difficulty could have been noted because the sense of smell was obscured by holding the nose.*

ACTIVITY 5-3: Reflex Actions (page 87)

OBJECTIVE: To demonstrate a reflex and show that it is automatic

CLASS TIME ALLOTMENT: 10 minutes.

MATERIALS:

plastic sheet, clear   cotton balls

PREPARATION NOTES:

In this activity the student studies the reflex that occurs when an object is thrown at a person. You may wish to have two students do this activity under your supervision in front of the class as a demonstration. Point out the defensive value of closing the eyes when a missile comes towards the eyes.

PROCEDURE:

Stand in front of the class with a sheet of clear plastic in front of your face. Have another student throw small cotton balls or crumpled paper at the plastic.

OBSERVATIONS AND DATA:

The student behind the plastic will blink at the cotton balls being tossed at him or her. He or she may also attempt to duck by moving the head. This same pattern of blinking (and possible ducking) will continue each time a cotton ball is thrown at the person.

QUESTIONS AND CONCLUSIONS:

This response is known as a reflex. It occurs naturally with no thought or direction coming from the brain. Most reflexes are protective. That is, they tend to have some protective value for the person. In this example, the eyes and head are being protected from a possible harmful injury.
1. What was your reaction? *eyelids closing, head moving*
2. What was the stimulus? *moving cotton balls*
3. Was this a learned behavior? Explain. *no, this is a reflex action*

ADDITIONAL QUESTIONS:

4. Give examples of other reflex actions. *coughing, sneezing, swallowing, yawning*
5. Are all examples that you listed actions that are automatic? *yes*

ACTIVITY 5-4: Knee Jerk (page 87)

OBJECTIVE: To cause and observe a reflex in the human body

CLASS TIME ALLOTMENT: 10 minutes.

MATERIALS: none

PREPARATION NOTES:

In this activity the student investigates the knee jerk reflex. Have students pair up to do this activity. They should take turns tapping each other's leg to produce the knee jerk response. Discuss the path the nerve impulse follows to produce the response.

PROCEDURE:

Sit down on a chair and cross your legs. Allow one leg to swing freely and relaxed. Then use the side of your hand to tap the area of your free leg just below the kneecap.

OBSERVATIONS AND DATA:

The leg will jerk up when the hand hits the area below the knee.

QUESTIONS AND CONCLUSIONS:

There is a nerve located in the area where the hand strikes the knee. This nerve is stretched slightly by the hand. It responds to this stretching by sending a message to muscles of the thigh. These thigh muscles shorten and cause the leg to jerk up, illustrating a reflex. The stretched nerve sends its message to the spinal cord. From the spinal cord, a new nerve carries the message to the proper muscle.

1. What happens? *the free leg jerks up*
2. What is the stimulus? *tap below the knee*
3. What is the response? *jerk*
4. Is this a reflex action? *yes*
5. Describe the path of the impulse. *knee to spinal cord to knee*

ADDITIONAL ACTIVITY: Eye Pupil Reflex (section 5:5)

OBJECTIVE: To observe how the pupil changes in size when light becomes bright or dull

CLASS TIME ALLOTMENT: 10 minutes.

MATERIALS:

mirror

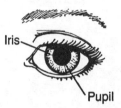

FIGURE 5-1

PREPARATION NOTES:

Advise students of the location of the pupil of the eye. Also tell them that the iris or colored part of the eye is a muscle. As this muscle relaxes or contracts, it changes the size of the pupil opening. A student who wears glasses may watch another student's eyes.

PROCEDURE:

1. Cover one eye with your hand. Keep both eyes open.
2. Have a mirror in front of you so that you can look at your eye immediately after you remove your hand.
3. Keep the eye covered for about 15 seconds.
4. Remove the hand and quickly note the change in size of your eye's pupil.
5. Repeat the experiment several times until you are sure of the change that is taking place. See if you can control the change that is occurring or whether it seems to be automatic.

OBSERVATIONS AND DATA:

While the eye is covered, little light is available. The iris opens the pupil as wide as possible to receive as much light as possible. When the hand is removed, bright light becomes available. The iris closes partially making the pupil smaller. The pupil no longer has to remain wide open because more light is now present.

QUESTIONS AND CONCLUSIONS:

All changes that occur with the iris are automatic. This muscle changes in shape depending on light conditions. It is a reflex and is not under your direct control.

1. (a) What size was the pupil while the eye was in the dark? *large*
   (b) Was the eye receiving much or little light at this time? *little*
2. (a) What size was the pupil when the eye received light? *small*
   (b) Was the eye receiving much or little light at this time? *much*
3. Explain how the pupil can change its shape if it is only a hole in the eye.
   The iris is a muscle that changes its shape. The iris surrounds the pupil making it appear as if the pupil is changing.
4. Is the change of pupil size automatic or under your control? *automatic*
5. (a) Does change in pupil size have any protective value? *yes*
   (b) Explain. *If one were to receive too much bright light, damage could occur to the retina of the eye. By reducing light, the eye is protected.*

ACTIVITY 5-5: Changing a Stimulus (page 88)

OBJECTIVE: To investigate a conditioned reflex by changing the stimulus

CLASS TIME ALLOTMENT: 20 minutes.

MATERIALS:

ruler

PREPARATION NOTES:

In this activity the student investigates a conditioned reflex by changing the stimulus from the spoken word "write" to the tap noise made by the ruler striking a chair. Have students count the number of times the ruler-writing sequence must be repeated before the ruler tapping became enough of a stimulus to produce a response.

PROCEDURE:

Stand behind a friend seated at a desk. Ask the friend to respond by drawing a line on a piece of paper each time you say "write." Every time you say "write" tap the chair or desk with the ruler. Do this about twenty times. Now, tap the ruler but do not use the stimulus "write."

OBSERVATIONS AND DATA:

Some students will have 20 lines on their paper. Others will have 21, 22, or 23.

QUESTIONS AND CONCLUSIONS:

Those students having more than 20 lines were conditioned. They associated the word stimulus with the sound stimulus. Once the word stimulus stopped but the sound stimulus continued, they still responded in the same manner.
1. Have you produced a conditioned reflex in your friend? *yes*
2. How does a behavior become a conditioned reflex? *new stimulus was substituted for original stimulus; response constant*

ADDITIONAL QUESTIONS:

3. What was the stimulus in this experiment? *the word "write" and the tapping sound*

4. What was the response?   *drawing a line on a piece of paper*
5. A conditioned reflex is one in which a new stimulus takes the place of the original stimulus. At what point in the experiment did a conditioned reflex occur?   *when the student wrote down the mark on command from the sound only*

ADDITIONAL ACTIVITY: Explaining a Habit (section 5:10)

OBJECTIVE: To teach another student a habit

CLASS TIME ALLOTMENT: 15 minutes.

MATERIALS: string—30 cm long

PREPARATION NOTES:
Remind students that a habit is a learned pattern of behavior that is done without thinking about how to do it. A behavior that becomes a habit first must be learned. It becomes automatic only as a result of constant repetition.

PROCEDURE:
1. Team students into groups of two.
2. Instruct one person in each team to hold a piece of string.
3. The other student is to now instruct the one holding the string how to correctly tie a square knot. The instructors cannot use their hands, therefore, they cannot touch or point to what the other person is doing. They can only tell them what to do.
4. Put a time limit of 2 minutes on the activity.
5. Change roles and repeat.

OBSERVATIONS AND DATA:
Few students will be able to complete the task in 2 minutes.

QUESTIONS AND CONCLUSIONS:
Tying a square knot (or neck tie, or bow tie, or shoelaces) is difficult to describe to someone else but easily done by yourself. These activities are habits and are therefore learned by us after many trials. Once mastered, however, the activities are almost automatic with little thought needed to complete them.
1. Were you able to correctly tie a square knot in two minutes when receiving instruction?   *may vary—probably no*
2. Were you able to correctly give instructions in two minutes to teach someone else to tie a square knot?   *may vary—probably no*
3. (a) Tying a knot is a habit. Is it difficult for you to do yourself?   *no*
   (b) Might it have been difficult for you to do when first learning?   *yes*
4. (a) Learning to ride a bicycle or roller skate are habits. Would you consider these activities at first to be simple or complex?   *complex*
   (b) Are they now simple or complex to you?   *simple*
   (c) Could you easily explain how to ride a bicycle to someone else?   *no*

CHALLENGE: APPLYING SCIENTIFIC METHODS
The Sense of Taste and Smell

OBJECTIVE: To determine how taste and smell are related

CLASS TIME ALLOTMENT: 20 minutes.

MATERIALS:
food samples, at least 10

PREPARATION NOTES:

In this activity the student investigates the interrelationship of taste and smell. Food samples may consist of raw potato, carrot, bread, onion, celery, apple, green pepper, peanut, mint candy, pear, and sunflower seeds. Go over the entire procedure with students before starting. To facilitate handling of food samples, you may wish to place five food samples into plastic bags and distribute the bags to student pairs. NOTE: Two samples of each food are needed in each bag.

PROCEDURE:
Part A: Getting Started
1. You will be working in teams of two for this experiment. One student will do the experiment and will be called Student X. The other student will record all results and help run the experiment. This person will be called student Y.
2. Throughout the entire experiment, Student X will always have eyes closed.

Part B. Using Only the Sense of Smell
1. Student Y will let Student X only smell each food sample, one at a time. Student X will guess what the food is. Student Y will record all results. DO NOT tell Student X the results at this time.

Part C. Using the Sense of Taste Only
1. Student X still has eyes closed and will now hold nose closed.
2. Student Y will place a sample of each food into Student X's mouth. Do this one sample at a time.
3. Let Student X again try to name the food type.
4. Record if Student X's answers are correct or wrong. DO NOT tell Student X the results at this time.

Part D. Using Both Taste and Smell at the Same Time
1. Student X still has eyes closed, but can now use sense of smell.
2. Student Y will give Student X a sample of each food, one at a time, to taste and smell.
3. Student Y will record if each guess is correct or wrong.

Part E. Repeating the Experiment
Parts A through D will be repeated except that
   (a) five new foods will be used and
   (b) students will change roles.

OBSERVATIONS AND DATA:

Student answers will vary. However, the number of correct answers should increase with the use of both smell and taste.

QUESTIONS AND CONCLUSIONS:

1. How many correct answers did you get using
   (a) only the sense of smell? *Student answers will vary.*
   (b) only the sense of taste? *Student answers will vary.*
   (c) smell and taste together? *Student answers will vary.*
2. Would you agree with the statement the smell and taste seem to depend on each other? Explain your answer. *Yes, more foods were correctly identified using both smell and taste.*

UNIT TWO

Human Health

chapter 6
Nutrition

ACTIVITY 6-1: Do You Eat a Balanced Diet? (page 104)

OBJECTIVE: To determine if students are eating foods from the four food groups (meat, milk, vegetable-fruit, and bread-cereal)

CLASS TIME ALLOTMENT: 10 minutes first day, 15 minutes discussion one week later.

MATERIALS:

PREPARATION NOTES:

In this activity the student compares the foods he or she eats with the basic four food groups. Have students construct the list of foods they eat, and then have them check each food against the basic four food groups.

PROCEDURE:

List the foods you eat each day for a week. Check each food against the four food groups. Save this list of foods to use later.

OBSERVATIONS AND DATA:

Each student's diet will differ when compared to other students. A proper diet will consist of foods eaten each day from all four food groups.

QUESTIONS AND CONCLUSIONS:

1. Did you eat a food from each of the four food groups?   *will vary*
2. If not, what was missing?   *will vary*

ADDITIONAL QUESTIONS:

3. Which of the four food groups seems to be missing most often from your classmates' diets?   *probably vegetable-fruit group*

ACTIVITY 6-2: Starch or Sugar? (page 108)

OBJECTIVE: To test various food samples for starch and sugar

CLASS TIME ALLOTMENT: One period.

MATERIALS:

beaker, 600 mL	marking pencil	food samples:
Benedict's solution	matches	apple juice
burner	test tube holder	bread
2 droppers	test tube rack	candy
glass dinner plate	6 test tubes	carrot
graduated cylinder, 10 mL	ring stand/ring	cornstarch
knife	water	corn syrup
iodine solution	wire screen	egg white, hard-boiled
		milk
		potato
		rice

PREPARATION NOTES:

In this activity the student tests various food samples for starch and sugar. Remind students to label the test tubes with a marking pencil so they can keep track of the contents of each test tube. Remind students to use small amounts of the food samples. Explain how to set up and use the hot water bath in Step 5. Caution students to use the test tube clamp to remove the hot test tubes from the water. A beaker may be used to hold the test tubes in Steps 3 and 4 if a test tube rack is not available. See Preparation of Solutions in Teacher's Guide for Benedict's and iodine solutions.

PROCEDURE:

1. Put a small amount of potato, egg white, rice, bread, cereal, candy, carrot, and cornstarch on the glass plate.
2. Add a drop of iodine solution to each food sample. Observe and record any color changes.
3. Label the test tubes A, B, C, D, E, and F. Add 5 mL of Benedict's solution to each test tube.
4. Add the following to the test tubes as indicated.
   A—4 drops corn syrup   D—5 mL apple juice
   B—small piece of candy   E—small piece of egg white
   C—small piece of bread   F—2 mL milk
5. Fill the beaker half full of water and bring the water to a boil using the burner. Place the test tubes in the hot water. Let them stand for 5 minutes.
6. Remove the test tubes from the hot water with the test tube holder. Observe and record any color changes.

OBSERVATIONS AND DATA:

FOOD SAMPLE/ TEST TUBE	COLOR CHANGE
A	

QUESTIONS AND CONCLUSIONS:

1. If starch is present, the brown-red color of iodine changes to a deep blue-black. Which foods contained starch?   *bread, cornstarch, potato, rice*
2. To what basic food group does each food sample that contained starch belong?   *carbohydrates*
3. What foods contained sugar? How do you know? (HINT: What happened to the Benedict's solution?)   *apple juice, candy, corn syrup; the Benedict's solution changed color*
4. What is the test for starch? What is the test for glucose?   *change of color in the iodine solution from brown to blue-black; change of color of Benedict's solution from blue to green, yellow, orange, and orange-red*

ACTIVITY 6-3: Which Foods are Rich in Fats? (page 109)

OBJECTIVE: To test samples of food to find out if they contain fat

CLASS TIME ALLOTMENT: 20 minutes.

MATERIALS:
paper, brown, unglazed
vegetable oil
margarine
butter
peanut butter
cheese
bacon
banana
salad dressing

PREPARATION NOTES:

In this activity the student tests samples of food to find out if they contain fat. Remind students to use only small amounts of the food samples. Provide paper towels for students for wiping fingers after testing a food sample. Direct students to record their observations and then go over the data that is provided.

PROCEDURE:

Obtain a piece of unglazed paper, such as brown wrapping paper. Hold the paper up to a light. Does any light come through the paper? Now rub some fat or oil on the paper. Again, hold the paper up to a light. What change has occurred? This smear test is the test for fats. Test samples of margarine, butter, peanut butter, cheese, bacon, banana, and salad dressing to see if these foods contain fats or oils.

OBSERVATIONS AND DATA:

FOOD	LIGHT PASSES THROUGH? (USE YES OR NO)	FAT PRESENT? (USE YES OR NO)
Margarine	yes	yes
Butter	yes	yes
Peanut butter	yes	yes
Cheese	yes	yes
Bacon	yes	yes
Salad dressing	yes	yes
Banana	yes	yes

All of the foods tested above contain fat.

QUESTIONS AND CONCLUSIONS:

1. Does any light come through brown wrapping paper?   *no*
2. Does any light come through brown wrapping paper after fat or oil has been rubbed on it?   *yes*
3. Which foods contained fats or oils?   *vegetable oil, margarine, butter, peanut butter, cheese, bacon, banana, salad dressing*

ADDITIONAL QUESTIONS:

4. Describe how to test a food for the presence of fats.   *The food is rubbed on brown paper. After drying, if a spot that allows light to pass through is left, the food contains fat.*
5. A lunchbag often has "grease stains" on it. Explain what those stains might be.   *The stains are probably spots left by fat on the paper. The lunch inside may have food that contains fat.*

ACTIVITY 6-4: Testing for Vitamin C (page 112)

OBJECTIVE: To test fruit juices for vitamin C and compare the vitamin C content of the juices

CLASS TIME ALLOTMENT: One period.

MATERIALS:

graduated cylinder
methylene blue
test tube
dropper

orange jucie
lemon juice
grapefruit juice
lime juice

PREPARATION NOTES:

In this activity the student tests fruit juices for vitamin C and compares the vitamin C content of the juices. Remind the students to rinse the dropper before they test a fruit juice. A chemical reaction between vitamin C and methylene blue turns the methylene blue colorless. The greater the vitamin C content of a fruit juice, the fewer the drops of juice needed to change the color. See Preparation of Solutions in Teacher's Guide for methylene blue.

PROCEDURE:

1. Add 10 mL of methylene blue solution to a test tube.
2. Use a dropper and add a drop of fresh orange jucie to the test tube. Gently swirl the test tube.
3. Continue to add orange juice to the test tube one drop at a time. Swirl the test tube after every addition. Count the number of drops of orange juice needed to change the color of the solution from blue to colorless.
4. Record this number.
5. Repeat Steps 1-3 using lemon juice, grapefruit juice, and lime juice.
6. Record the number of drops of each juice needed to turn the methylene blue solution colorless.

OBSERVATIONS AND DATA:

JUICE TESTED	NUMBER OF DROPS NEEDED TO TURN METHYLENE BLUE COLORLESS	MOST OR LEAST VITAMIN C PRESENT
Orange juice		
Lemon juice		
Grapefruit juice		
Lime juice		

The number of drops of juice needed will vary.

QUESTIONS AND CONCLUSIONS:

1. Which juice contains the most vitamin C?   *will vary*
2. Which juice contains the least vitamin C?   *will vary*

The fewer the number of drops needed to change methylene blue from its original color to colorless, the more vitamin C is present in the juice.

ACTIVITY 6-5: Calories (page 113)

OBJECTIVE: To calculate the daily intake of Calories and evaluate this figure in relation to the average minimum requirement

CLASS TIME ALLOTMENT: One period.

MATERIALS: none

PREPARATION NOTES:

In this activity the student calculates his or her daily intake of Calories and evaluates this figure in relation to the average minimum requirement. This activity can be done out of class and you may wish to make it a homework assignment. You may wish to make students aware of the fact that if they eat a great many deep-fried foods, they are adding extra Calories due to the fats used in deep frying which remain in the foods. Deep-frying is a method used by many fast-food restaurants.

PROCEDURE:

Use the Calorie Charts listed in Appendix C and the food list from the Activity on page 104. Calculate the number of Calories per day that you eat. Use the Calorie Charts and Figure 6-1 to write balanced meals for one week.

OBSERVATIONS AND DATA:

Daily Calorie requirements should total approximately 3000 for boys and 2500 for girls. Balanced diets should include foods from the four food groups.

QUESTIONS AND CONCLUSIONS:

Most Americans consume many "empty"Calories from foods high in carbohydrates (bread-cereal group and sweets). These often provide most of theCalories eaten each day.
1. Is the number of Calories per day that you eat higher or lower than the minimum requirement for your age group?   *Answers will vary.*
2. What food group provides most of the Calories you eat?   *carbohydrates (bread-cereal) may provide most of the calories*

ADDITIONAL QUESTIONS:

3. What is meant by a balanced diet?   *one that includes food from each of the four food groups in appropriate quantities*

ACTIVITY 6-6: Food Labels (page 117)

OBJECTIVE: To learn what information is given about food on a label

CLASS TIME ALLOTMENT: 20 minutes.

MATERIALS:
food labels, 10

PREPARATION NOTES:

In this activity the student studies food package labels to learn what information they contain. Have students draw the data table in their notebooks before starting this activity. An alternative approach is to make photocopies of labels and distribute these to students. Go over the data table using one food label as an example to be certain students understand what kind of information should be recorded in each column.

PROCEDURE:

1. Collect the labels from 10 of your favorite processed foods.
2. Fill in the blanks in your data table with the information for each food.

OBSERVATIONS AND DATA:

| NAME OF FOOD | THREE MAIN INGRE- DIENTS | CALO- RIES/ SERV- ING | AMOUNT | | | ARTIFI- CIAL SUB- STANCES ADDED |
			FAT	PRO- TEIN	CARBO- HY- DRATES	

QUESTIONS AND CONCLUSIONS:

1. What was the main natural ingredient in each food?   *Answers will vary.*
2. To which basic food group does each food belong?   *Refer students to the four food groups.*
3. If you ate portions of these 10 foods in one day, would you eat a balanced diet? Explain.   *Refer students to the four food groups.*
4. If you ate one serving of each of these 10 foods in one day, would you exceed the number of Calories your body needs? Explain.   *Refer students to the caloric value of the foods and their daily Calorie requirement.*
5. Which foods would you recommend to a person who is trying to lose weight? Why?   *foods low in carbohydrates and fats; these have fewer calories*
6. Which food(s) contained additives?   *probably each food unless the package was labeled as having no additives*
7. What was the most common additive?   *Answers will vary but may be salt or sugar.*
8. Did any of the foods have added vitamins? Which foods?   *Answers will vary.*

CHALLENGE: APPLYING SCIENTIFIC METHODS
Water Content of Food

OBJECTIVE: To determine the percentage of water in several food samples

CLASS TIME ALLOTMENT: 10 minutes one day, 20 minutes the next day.

MATERIALS:

aluminum tray	carrot, thin slice
balance	labels or marking pencil
beans, 10	lettuce
bread slice	light source, 100 watt

PREPARATION NOTES:

In this activity, students compare the mass of several food samples before and after heating to determine the water content of the samples. Use a goose-neck lamp or a heat lamp for the light source. An incubator may also be substituted for the lamp.

PROCEDURE:

1. Use a balance to determine the mass of each food sample and record.
2. Label an aluminum tray with your name.
3. Place your food samples on the tray and place under a lighted light source. Leave undisturbed overnight.
4. The following day, remass each food sample and record.
5. For each food sample, subtract the mass after heating from the mass of the sample before heating. Record the loss of mass for each sample.
6. To determine the percentage of water in each sample, divide the mass of the sample before heating into the loss of mass for that sample. Carry your division to two places only. Multiply your answer by 100.

OBSERVATIONS AND DATA:

Student data will vary. However, all food samples should have less mass after heating than before. A slice of bread is about 50% water, carrots are about 36% water, and the beans are about 8% water.

QUESTIONS AND CONCLUSIONS:

1. (a) Which food sample had the largest loss in mass after heating?   *Bread had the largest loss in mass after heating.*
   (b) Which food sample had the largest percentage of water?   *Bread had the largest percentage of water (50%).*
2. (a) Which food sample had the smallest loss in mass after heating?   *The beans had the smallest loss of mass after heating.*
   (b) Which food sample had the smallest percentage of water?   *The beans had the smallest percentage of water (8%).*
3. Why do the food samples lose mass when placed under a light?   *The heat from the lamp causes the water to evaporate from the food samples.*
4. How might the skin on a potato or an apple affect water loss?   *The skin retards water loss.*
5. A watermelon has a mass of 5 000 g. After heating, its mass is 400 g.
   (a) How much water did the melon lose?   *4 600 g*
   (b) What percentage of this food is water?   *92%*

---

chapter 7

Disease

ACTIVITY 7-1: Growing Microbes on Agar (page 126)

OBJECTIVE: To observe the difference in the growth of bacteria

CLASS TIME ALLOTMENT: 15 minutes on day one, 5 minutes on day two, 15 minutes three days later.

MATERIALS:

petri dishes with nutrient agar, 4   soap
marking pencil   paper towel

PREPARATION NOTES:

In this activity the student inoculates sterile petri dishes with a washed and an unwashed finger and observes the difference in the growth of bacteria. Follow the directions for preparing nutrient agar given on the package, or see Preparation of Solutions. Have students label the dishes A, B, C, and D. Caution students not to open the dishes after they have been sealed.

PROCEDURE:

1. Obtain 4 covered sterile petri dishes containing nutrient agar. Label the dishes A, B, C, and D.

2. Open dish A and rub a finger of your right hand over the agar surface. Reseal the dish. Wash and dry your hands.
3. Open dish B and rub a finger of your left hand over the agar surface. Reseal the dish.
4. Open dish C and leave uncovered and undisturbed overnight.
5. Leave dish D sealed.
6. The next day, reseal dish C and place the 4 dishes in a warm place for several days.
7. Observe and explain any changes that occur on the surface of the agar. After the activity, return the dishes unopened to your teacher.

OBSERVATIONS AND DATA:

An agar surface provides bacteria with their nutritional needs and they begin to reproduce. In 24 hours you can see clumps or colonies of bacteria on the agar surface.

A just-washed finger should show fewer colonies than an unwashed finger. A dish open to the air will show many colonies because bacteria are present in the air. The unopened dish serves as a control and should have no bacterial colonies on it.

QUESTIONS AND CONCLUSIONS:

Bacteria are too small to be seen with unaided eye. If provided with food, moisture, and proper temperature, they will increase rapidly in number. (It may take only 20 minutes to form a new generation.) This rapid reproduction of bacteria (formation of colonies) eventually enables observation with the unaided eye.
1. What is the control for this experiment?   *the covered dish*

ADDITIONAL QUESTIONS:

2. What was seen on the agar surface that was not present at the start of the experiment?   *groups or colonies of bacteria*
3. Why are some bacteria dangerous to humans?   *They cause disease.*
4. Are bacteria present in the air?   *yes*
5. Can disease be spread through the air?   *yes*

CHALLENGE: APPLYING SCIENTIFIC METHODS
Microbe Control

OBJECTIVE: To determine the effectiveness of mouthwash and rubbing alcohol in controlling microbes.

CLASS TIME ALLOTMENT: One period.

MATERIALS:

burner	methylene blue	test tube rack
dropper	mouthwash	test tube clamp
goggles	rubbing alcohol	yeast solution
graduated cylinder	stoppers, to fit test tubes	water
marking pencil	test tubes	watch or clock

PREPARATION NOTES:

In this activity, students determine the effectiveness of mouthwash and rubbng alcohol in controlling yeast, which represent microbes. Methylene blue is used as an oxygen indicator. Methylene blue remains blue in the presence of oxygen, but turns light blue to colorless as oxygen decreases. To prepare methylene blue, dissolve 1.0 g methylene blue powder in 1.0 L distilled water. Prepare yeast solution by dissolving one cake of yeast or one package of dry yeast in 200 mL distilled water. Caution students to wear goggles while heating test tubes. You may wish to boil one-fourth of the yeast solution prior to class.

PROCEDURE:

1. Put 2 mL yeast solution in a test tube. Using a clamp to hold it, pass this tube through the flame of a burner until the yeast boils. Remove from flame and allow to cool. Repeat boiling at least four times.
2. Number 4 test tubes 1 through 4 and place them in a test tube rack.
3. Add the following to each tube:
   Tube 1—10 drops boiled yeast
   Tube 2—10 drops unboiled yeast
   Tube 3—10 drops unboiled yeast and 10 drops rubbing alcohol
   Tube 4—10 drops unboiled yeast and 10 drops mouthwash
4. Add 5 mL water and 5 drops methylene blue to each tube.
5. Stopper each tube and gently mix.
6. Note the color in each tube and record. Use only the words medium blue, light blue, or colorless in recording each observation.
7. Wait exactly 5 minutes and again note the colors in all tubes. Record the colors again. It may be helpful to hold all four tubes together toward the light so that slight changes in color may be detected. For best results, compare all tubes with tube 1.
8. Repeat steps 7 for three more five minute periods and record your results.
9. Label the test tube rack with your name and leave overnight. The next day, note, compare, and record the colors of all tubes.

OBSERVATIONS AND DATA:

Tube 1 should remain blue throughout the experiment. Tube 2 should change from medium blue to light blue to colorless. Tubes 3 and 4 also remain medium blue throughout the experiment.

QUESTIONS AND CONCLUSIONS:

1. What were the yeast representing in this experiment?   *microbes, such as bacteria*
2. (a) Did the yeast in tube 1 change color?   *no*
   (b) Were yeast using oxygen in this tube?   *no*
   (c) Were yeast alive in this tube?   *no*
   (d) What happened when you boiled the yeast four or five times?   *The yeast were killed.*
3. (a) In which tube(s) did the blue color change from medium to light or colorless?   *Tube 2*
   (b) Were yeast using oxygen in this (these) tube(s)?   *yes*
   (c) Were yeast alive or dead in this (these) tube(s)?   *alive*

4. (a) Which tube(s) other than 1 did not change in color?   *Tubes 3 and 4*
   (b) Were these yeast using oxygen?   *no*
   (c) What is your proof?   *There was no color changes in the tubes.*
   (d) What was added to this (these) tube(s) that may have killed them?
       Rubbing alcohol and mouthwash were added to these tubes.
5. Did the mouthwash and alcohol used in this experiment kill yeast?   *yes*

EXTENSION:

Have students repeat the experiment using other household items such as dishwashing liquid, household cleaners, etc.

---

chapter 8

Drugs

ACTIVITY 8-1: Drug Survey (page 142)

OBJECTIVE: To study labels of nonprescription drug containers to learn the names and uses of each drug, recommended dosage, and any warnings related to the use of the drug

CLASS TIME ALLOTMENT: 20 minutes.

MATERIALS:

nonprescription drug labels (5)

PREPARATION NOTES:

In this activity the student studies the labels from nonprescription drug containers to learn the names and uses of each drug, recommended dosage, and any warnings related to the use of the drug. Stress the importance of knowing the contents of a nonprescription drug, safe dosage, and warnings, such as not to use a given drug prior to driving or using machinery. Students may wish to survey a local drug store to learn the major uses of nonprescription drugs. Most nonprescription drugs contain at least one of the following: aspirin (or other pain relievers), antihistamine, or antacid. Nonprescription drugs are used primarily for headaches, allergies, colds, and upset stomach.

PROCEDURE:

Obtain the labels from 5 empty nonprescription drug containers. Do not open the containers. Record the name and use of each drug, the recommended dose, and any warnings on the label.

OBSERVATIONS AND DATA:

Most common nonprescription drugs may include aspirin, cold tablets, antacids, sleep aids, pain remedies, etc.

DRUG NAME	USE	RECOMMENDED DOSE	WARNINGS

QUESTIONS AND CONCLUSIONS:

1. Did any of the drugs have warnings on their labels?   *Answers will vary.*
2. What was the most common warning?   *Answers will vary.*

ADDITIONAL QUESTIONS:

3. Why is it important to take the recommended dosage?   *Too much or too little of a drug could produce harmful effects.*

ACTIVITY 8-2: Penicillin and Growth of Microbes (page 144)

OBJECTIVE: To investigate the effect of penicillin in preventing the growth of microorganisms

CLASS TIME ALLOTMENT: 20 minutes on each of two consecutive days.

MATERIALS:

petri dish with nutrient agar
marking pencil
penicillin disks of different strengths (3)
forceps
sterile paper disk

PREPARATION NOTES:

In this activity the student investigates the effect of penicillin in preventing the growth of microorganisms. Direct students to record their observations in their notebooks. Explain that the dishes will be collected unopened at the end of the activity. Dispose of cultures in a safe manner. Penicillin may be obtained from a biological supply house. See Preparation of Solutions in the Teacher's Guide for instructions on preparing penicillin and agar. Allow the disks to drain before students place them on the agar. The untreated sterile disk will serve as a control. Prepare the sterile nutrient agar dishes the day prior to doing this activity.

PROCEDURE:

1. Obtain a covered petri dish containing sterile nutrient agar. With a marking pencil, divide the dish into 4 quarters by marking on the outside of the dish. Label the quarters A, B, C, and D.
2. Obtain 3 penicillin disks of differing strengths from your teacher.

3. Open your petri dish. Use forceps to place each disk in the center of a separate quarter of your agar dish. Add a plain sterile paper disk to the remaining quarter. Record the strengths of the penicillin disk placed in each quarter.
4. Expose the open dish to the air overnight.
5. Cover the dish and seal it with tape.
6. Place the dish in a warm spot or in an incubator at 37°C for several days.
7. Observe and explain the bacteria growth patterns.

OBSERVATIONS AND DATA:

After several days, the petri dish will have many bacterial colonies on its surface. A clear ring of no bacterial growth will appear around the disks. The disks having the widest clear zone were most effective in preventing bacterial growth.

QUESTIONS AND CONCLUSIONS:

Chemicals (penicillin) present on the disks prevented bacteria from growing. When physicians prescribe an antibiotic for a patient, they are relying on this same principle that the antibiotic will stop the growth of the bacteria.
1. Do some disks appear to have a clear zone around them?   *yes*
2. What does this clear area mean?   *No bacteria were able to grow because of the penicillin (antibiotic) present in the disk.*
3. What might have been the results if only untreated paper disks were used?   *Bacteria would grow near the paper disk.*

ADDITIONAL ACTIVITY: Testing Cigarette Tars on Living Organisms (section 8:4)

OBJECTIVE: To determine if cigarette tars have a harmful effect on living protozoa

CLASS TIME ALLOTMENT: One period.

MATERIALS:

cigarette
gravy baster (from home, hardware store)
flask, 500 mL
glass bends (as shown in diagram) (2)
glass slides and coverslips
living protozoa or living brine shrimp, water fleas (from biological supply house)
marking pencil

match
microscope
rubber tubing, 1 long length
rubber tubing, 1 short length
stopper to fit flask, 2-hole
tape

PREPARATION NOTES:

The first part of this activity (Steps 1-4) is designed as a teacher demonstration.

PROCEDURE:

1. Set up a smoking machine as shown in the diagram.

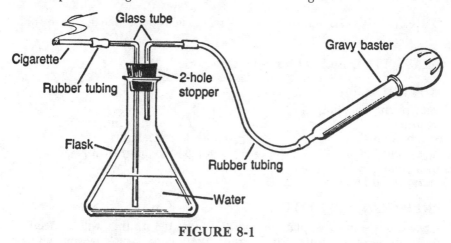

FIGURE 8-1

2. Place 100 mL of water in the flask. Make sure that long glass tube extends below water surface.
3. Light the cigarette. By pressing on the gravy baster bulb, air will be forced in and out of the flask. As air is pulled in, smoke and chemicals from the cigarette will be pulled into the water of the flask.
4. When the cigarette is finished, remove stopper from flask. Pour water into small beakers for student use.
5. Prepare 2 glass slides for microscope examination. One slide receives a drop or two of living protozoa and a coverslip. Mark this slide "water." Use a marking pencil or a small piece of tape. Other slide receives a drop or two of living protozoa plus a drop of cigarette water and a coverslip. Mark this slide "cigarette."
6. Examine both slides under the microscope. Use only low power magnification.
7. Compare the amount of activity of the protozoans on both slides.

OBSERVATIONS AND DATA:

The cigarette water when added to the protozoa will stop all movement. Actually, the protozoa are killed by the chemical present in cigarette smoke and tar. Protozoa in the untreated water will appear to be moving rapidly.

QUESTIONS AND CONCLUSIONS:

Nicotine is a poisonous chemical present in cigarette smoke. Nicotine is used as an insecticide and is harmful to other organisms.

1. Describe the movement of protozoa under the microscope when in untreated water.   *They move about rapidly.*
2. Describe the movement of protozoa under the microscope in cigarette water.   *They do not move.*
3. Why might the protozoa react to the cigarette water as they did?   *They were killed.*
4. How might cigarette smoke and tars affect living cells of a human's lungs or throat?   *possibly in the same manner*

CHALLENGE: APPLYING SCIENTIFIC METHODS
Cigarette Tars

OBJECTIVE: To determine if tars from cigarette smoke are harmful to plants

CLASS TIME ALLOTMENT: One period.

MATERIALS:

bean plants, seedlings
cigarette
cotton swabs
gallon jugs, 2
glass tubing, 5 cm
 and 10 cm lengths

matches
rubber tubing, 5 cm, 10 cm,
 and 25 cm lengths
stopper, 2-hole to fit jugs
water

PREPARATION NOTES:

Seedlings should be planted about 10 days before they will be needed. Soak pinto beans in water for 24 hours, then plant in sand, vermiculite, or soil and keep moist. Other plants besides beans may also be used. Provide each student with a separate swab of tars, using a new cigarette for each team. To help show the results of tars on plants and to insure more dramatic results, use cigarettes without filters and rub the tars from three or four cigarettes onto the plant. You may wish to use this activity as a demonstration.

PROCEDURE:

Part A: Building and Using the Smoking Machine

1. Assemble the necessary parts to look like Figure 8-2. **CAUTION:** Always moisten glass tubing with water or glycerine before inserting in stopper. Wrap your hands in cloth toweling and gently twist the glass tubing into the stopper hole.

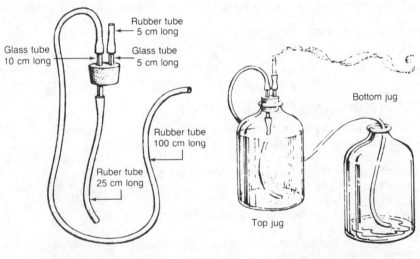

Glass tube 10 cm long

Rubber tube 5 cm long

Glass tube 5 cm long

Rubber tube 100 cm long

Ruber tube 25 cm long

Bottom jug

Top jug

FIGURE 8-2   **FIGURE 8-3**

2. Fill a gallon jug with water. Place the stopper with tubing into this jug. Position a second empty jug on the classroom floor.
3. Place a cigarette in the opening of the short rubber tube.
4. Pull some water through the long rubber tube with your mouth and quickly put the end of the long tube into the empty jug on the floor.
5. After the water begins flowing from the top jug to the bottom jug, light the cigarette (Figure 8-3).
6. When the cigarette is finished, stop the flow of water. Do this by lifting the long rubber tube from the bottom jug.

Part B: Removing and Using the Cigarette Tar
1. Remove the remains of the cigarette. **CAUTION:** Wait until the cigarette has completely cooled.
2. Take a cotton swab and clean the inside of the short tubing that held the cigarette. Note the color and odor of tar that remains on the swab. Record your observations.
3. Rub these chemical tars on a young bean plant. Ask your teacher which treatment you are to use. You may
   (a) rub a complete ring of tar around the plant's stem.
   (b) rub tar onto only one large leaf.
   (c) rub tar onto the young growing tip only.
4. Observe the plant for several days and note any changes that take place. Record your observations.

OBSERVATIONS AND DATA:

Student answers will vary depending on the treatment the student used. In all cases, there should be a visible, deleterious effect on the plant. The plant stem may turn brown and become dry. The same effect may be seen on the plant leaf. There should be little or no growth of the plant tip.

QUESTIONS AND CONCLUSIONS:

Are tars harmful to plants? Explain.   *Student answers will depend upon the type of treatment used. In all cases, there will be deleterious effects.*

---

chapter 9

Human Reproduction and Heredity

ACTIVITY 9-1: Tongue Rolling (page 167)

OBJECTIVE: To determine who can or cannot roll their tongue and to see how class totals agree with expected totals

CLASS TIME ALLOTMENT: 20 minutes.

MATERIALS:

PREPARATION NOTES:

In this activity students survey the class to find out which students can and cannot roll their tongues. Tongue rolling is an inherited trait. One procedure to follow in doing this activity is to pair students and have them observe each other's tongue-rolling ability. On the chalkboard record the number of tongue rollers and nonrollers and compute the percentage of rollers. Compare this percentage figure with the general population average of 70% rollers.

PROCEDURE:

One dominant human trait is the ability to roll the edges of the tongue into a U-shape. Survey your classmates to see how many of them can roll their tongues. Record the number of students that can roll their tongues.

OBSERVATIONS AND DATA:

On the average about 3 out of 10 people cannot roll their tongues.

	EXPECTED	NUMBER OF STUDENTS OBSERVED	PERCENTAGE OF STUDENTS OBSERVED
Tongue rollers	70%		
Nonrollers	30%		

QUESTIONS AND CONCLUSIONS:

1. How many students cannot roll their tongues?   *Answers will vary.*
2. On the average, about 3 out of 10 people cannot roll their tongues. How does your class compare to this figure?   *Answers will vary.*

ADDITIONAL QUESTIONS:

3. Are you a roller or nonroller?   *will vary*
4. Are your results wrong if they do not agree exactly with the 70/30% expected?   *no*
5. What percentage might you observe if 1000 students were in your class? *very close to 70% rollers and 30% nonrollers*

ADDITIONAL ACTIVITY: A Pedigree for Tongue Rollers (section 9:5)

OBJECTIVE: To draw a pedigree for the family described below.

CLASS TIME ALLOTMENT: 20 minutes.

MATERIALS:

PREPARATION NOTES:

Both parents in a family are tongue rollers. They have three offspring—two sons and a daughter. All the offspring are tongue rollers. The daughter marries a man who is a tongue roller. They have one son and three daughters. All are tongue rollers except one daughter.

PROCEDURE:

1. The pedigree to be drawn for the family must observe these rules:
   (a) males are shown with squares, females with circles;
   (b) a marriage is shown with a line connecting the two parents;
   (c) children are shown with a vertical line from the marriage line with a horizontal line connecting the children shown; and
   (d) persons who show the dominant trait (tongue rolling) are shaded in.
2. Persons are marked A-J to help identify who they are.

OBSERVATIONS AND DATA:

Student pedigrees should appear like this.

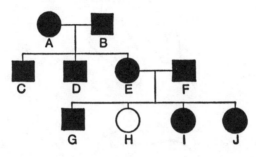

FIGURE 9-1

QUESTIONS AND CONCLUSIONS:

The unshaded girl (H) could actually be any of the three sisters shown (H-J) and does not have to be the exact one in the example. All shaded persons have at least one dominant gene for tongue rolling. All unshaded persons have two recessive genes for the trait. Persons B and F are hybrid. They each carry a recessive gene. Either person A or B may also be a hybrid. However, enough information is not available in this family to identify the gene makeup for all other individuals with 100% accuracy.

1. (a) What does the shading of a person show?   *a dominant trait such as tongue rolling*
   (b) What does the unshading indicate?   *recessive trait such as no tongue rolling*
2. (a) Can an unshaded person be hybrid?   *no*
   (b) Can a shaded person be hybrid?   *yes*
   (c) Can a shaded person be pure dominant?   *yes*
   (d) Can you always tell if a shaded person is hybrid or pure dominant?   *no*

ACTIVITY 9-2: Handspan Size and its Inheritance (page 172)

OBJECTIVE: To measure the handspans of students and graph the data

CLASS TIME ALLOTMENT: 30 minutes.

MATERIALS:

graph paper   metric ruler

PREPARATION NOTES:

In this activity students measure the handspans of students and graph the data. From the graph, students will see the variation of handspans among the members of the class. These inherited variations can be explained by the trait being controlled by several pairs of genes. Any kind of paper may be used if graph paper is not available.

PROCEDURE:

1. Spread out your hand on a piece of graph paper. Make a mark at the tip of your thumb and at the tip of your little finger. Do not include length of fingernails.

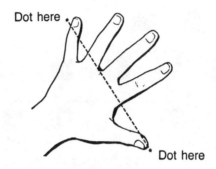

Dot here

FIGURE 9-2

Dot here

2. Measure the distance between the two marks (your handspan) in millimeters.
3. Record the handspan measurements of all members of your class on the chalkboard.
4. Organize the measurements into a table showing handspans in groups of 5 mm. Also record the number of students in each group.
5. Draw a graph of the data in the table.

OBSERVATIONS AND DATA:

NUMBER OF STUDENTS	HANDSPAN WIDTH
	Less than 170 mm
	170-175 mm
	176-180 mm
	181-185 mm
	186-190 mm
	191-195 mm
	196-200 mm
	201-205 mm
	206-210 mm
	211-215 mm
	216-220 mm
	221-225 mm
	226-230 mm
	231-235 mm
	236-240 mm
	241-245 mm
	over 245 mm

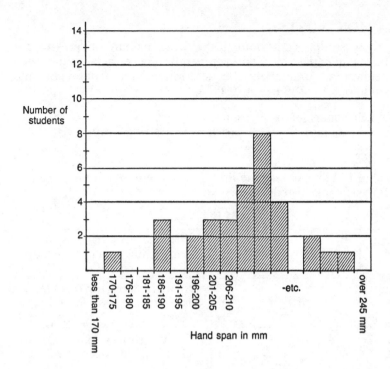

The handspan of students will vary. The majority of students should have a handspan of about 220 mm. This will be evident on the histogram.

QUESTIONS AND CONCLUSIONS:

If a genetic trait is controlled by a single pair of genes, then class results would usually show only two categories or groups. When a genetic trait is controlled by several pairs of genes, a number of different groups will appear. There were more than two groups of handspan widths. Therefore, this genetic trait must be controlled by more than one pair of genes.

1. What does the graph reveal about the differences in handspans within your class?   *There are wide variations.*
2. Based on your data, do you think hand size is controlled by one or more pairs of genes?   *several pairs of genes*
3. What other factors can affect hand size?   *rate of maturation, general body size, past health or accidents*

CHALLENGE: APPLYING SCIENTIFIC METHODS
A Self Survey

OBJECTIVE: To determine if you have the dominant or recessive condition of each of eleven human genetic traits, and to examine some genetic traits of plants.

CLASS TIME ALLOTMENT: 20 minutes.

PREPARATION NOTES:

In this activity, students determine if they are dominant or recessive for eleven different genetic traits. For your convenience, a table has been provided below that summarizes the description of the dominant and recessive conditions for the eleven traits.

MATERIALS: watermelon   squash   peas
tomato   peach   string beans

PROCEDURE:

1. Using Table 1 below, determine if you have the dominant or recessive condition for each trait listed. Record your observations.

TABLE 1

Eyelid shape		Oriental eye shape is dominant. Caucasian or negro eye shape is recessive.
Teeth position		Space between top front teeth is dominant. No space is recessive.
Chin shape		Cleft in chin is dominant. No cleft in chin is recessive.
Hair on fingers		Hair on middle part only of one or several fingers is dominant. No hair on middle part of fingers is recessive.
Tongue muscles		Ability to roll up sides of tongue with special muscles is dominant. Not being able to roll up sides is recessive.
White hair		A patch or streak of white hair is dominant. No patch of white hair is recessive.
Number of fingers		Having six fingers is dominant. Having five fingers is recessive.
Eye color		All dark eye colors are dominant. Blue or gray eye color is recessive.
Ear lobe shape		Having free ear lobes is dominant. Having attached ear lobes is recessive.
Handedness		If you are right handed, this is dominant. If you are left handed, this is recessive.
Hair color		Not having red hair is dominant. Having red hair is recessive.

2. Examine samples of several fruits and vegetables. Using Table 2, determine if the traits exhibited by these plants are dominant or recessive. Record your observations.

TABLE 2

Watermelon shape		Round is dominant. Long shape is recessive.
Watermelon color		Solid green on outside is dominant. Dark green stripes on outside is recessive.
Tomato color		Red is dominant. Yellow or orange is recessive.
Squash shape		Disk shape is dominant. Round shape is recessive.
Peach skin		Hairy skin is dominant. Smooth skin is recessive.
Peas		Peas that are perfectly round are dominant. Wrinkled peas are recessive.
Bean pod color		Green bean pods are dominant. Yellow bean pods are recessive.

OBSERVATIONS AND DATA:

Student answers will vary.

QUESTIONS AND CONCLUSIONS:

1. How many dominant traits of the eleven given do you have?   *Answers will vary.* Which traits are they?   *Answers will vary.*
2. How many recessive traits do you exhibit?   *Answers will vary.*
3. It is often assumed that a person who has a recessive trait has an abnormal trait. Does this statement seem to be true?   *No, dominant and recessive traits do not imply normal and abnormal.*
4. In your plant survey, how many dominant traits of the seven given did you see?   *Answers will vary.*
5. How many recessive traits did you see?   *Answers will vary.*
6. (a) Do humans only use plants for food that exhibit dominant traits?   *No, humans use plants having both dominant and recessive traits for food.*
   (b) Explain by using an example.   *Both disk-shaped (dominant) and round-shaped (recessive) squash are used for food.*
7. (a) If you were a farmer and wanted to grow only yellow tomatoes, with what kind of parent tomato plants would you start?   *One would start with parent plants that are yellow, thus exhibiting the recessive trait.*
   (b) Why?   *Because both parents are pure-bred recessives, the offspring will be pure-bred recessive.*

UNIT THREE

Chemistry

chapter 10
Matter

ACTIVITY 10-1: Physical Properties (page 185)

OBJECTIVE: To examine, record, and compare physical properties of aluminum, iron, rubber, and wood

CLASS TIME ALLOTMENT: 20 minutes.

MATERIALS:

conductivity apparatus	wood
aluminum	beaker, 500 mL
iron	ring stand/ring
rubber	

PREPARATION NOTES:

In this activity the student examines, records, and compares physical properties of aluminum, iron, ruber, and wood. It is recommended that this activity be done as a demonstration. You can purchase the conductivity apparatus at a science supply house. Testing for conductivity is done by touching the two electrodes of the apparatus to the material to be tested

CAUTION: Be careful not to touch the electrodes when the circuit is connected because you will receive a shock.

PROCEDURE:

Examine and record the physical properties of samples of aluminum, iron, rubber, and wood. Use a conductivity apparatus to determine if each sample is a conductor. Touch the electrodes to each sample in a beaker.

CAUTION: Do not touch the electrodes with your hands because you may receive a shock. Record your results.

OBSERVATIONS AND DATA:

Students may use their own words to describe the physical properties. Additional responses are fine.

SAMPLE	PHYSICAL PROPERTIES	CONDUCTOR? (YES OR NO)
Aluminum	solid, shiny, malleable	yes
Iron	solid, black, malleable	yes
Rubber	solid, lacks luster, not malleable	no
Wood	solid, lacks luster, not malleable	no

QUESTIONS AND CONCLUSIONS:

Many physical properties may be shared by the solids used in this activity. For example, aluminum and iron are malleable. Rubber and wood may be cut into different shapes.
1. What two properties do aluminum and iron have in common? *both are solids and conduct electricity*
2. What two physical properties do rubber and wood have in common? *both are solids and do not conduct electricity*

ACTIVITY 10-2: Chemical Change (page 185)

OBJECTIVE: To observe a chemical reaction

CLASS TIME ALLOTMENT: 30 minutes.

MATERIALS:

graduated cylinder, 10 mL
HC1, dilute
test tube, large
test tube rack
mossy zinc, 2 pieces

PREPARATION NOTES:

In this activity the student observes a chemical reaction and that heat is produced in the reaction. Hydrogen gas is another product. Have students observe the change in the size of the zinc pieces as they are consumed in the reaction.

PROCEDURE:

1. Pour 5 mL of dilute hydrochloric acid into a large test tube.
2. Touch the outside bottom of the test tube and record your impression of its temperature—cold, cool, warm, or hot.
3. Carefully add 2 small pieces of mossy zinc to the test tube. Observe and record what happens.
4. Touch the bottom of the test tube again and record your impression of the temperature.

OBSERVATIONS AND DATA:

	TEMPERATURE	OBSERVATIONS
Test tube before adding mossy zinc	*cool*	*none*
Test tube after adding mossy zinc	*warm (or hot)*	*bubbles given off*

QUESTIONS AND CONCLUSIONS:

Heat is sometimes produced in a chemical reaction. In this chemical change, zinc combined with the chloride and hydrogen gas was given off (bubbles), as well as heat. The new substance was zinc chloride.
1. What happened to the zinc?   *It was changed to another substance.*
2. Was the change in zinc a physical or chemical change?   *chemical change*
3. How do you know?   *heat released, gas produced*

ADDITIONAL ACTIVITY: A Common Chemical Change (section 10:2)

OBJECTIVE: To observe rusting, a common chemical change

CLASS TIME ALLOTMENT: 10 minutes first day, 5 minutes on next 3 days.

MATERIALS:

beaker	marking pencil	test tube
clamp and ring stand	iron filings	water

PREPARATION NOTES:

This activity demonstrates a common chemical change, rusting. Students observe a color change in iron filings over a three day period. The color change is caused by the combining of oxygen and iron to form rust.

PROCEDURE:

1. Moisten the inside of a test tube with water.
2. Sprinkle some iron filings into the tube.
3. Invert the test tube and lower it partway into a beaker of water.
4. Clamp in this position. Mark the water level in the test tube. NOTE: The initial water level can be marked with a glass marking pencil or with tape. This will be helpful in observing the changing level.
5. Observe for the next three days. Record your observations.

OBSERVATIONS AND DATA:

The iron filings turn rust-colored and crumble. The water level rises in the test tube.

DAY	OBSERVATIONS
1	
2	
3	

QUESTIONS AND CONCLUSIONS:

This reaction must be a chemical change because new and different substances are formed. The new substances have different properties than the original substance.

1. Explain why the iron filings change color.   *They combine with oxygen to form a new substance that has a different color. Rust is a common name for the new substance.*

2. Explain why water rises in the test tube.   *Oxygen in the air in the test tube is used when the iron reacts with it causing a reduction in pressure. The water moves up into the tube as a result of the change in pressure.*

ADDITIONAL ACTIVITY: Separating a Mixture into its Parts (section 10:4)

OBJECTIVE: To learn how to separate a mixture by distillation

CLASS TIME ALLOTMENT: One period.

MATERIALS:

beaker, 400 mL
boiling chip, marble
Bunsen burner or other heat source
clamps—3
condenser with cooling jacket
distilling flask with side-arm,
    500 mL
glycerin
goggles
graduated cylinder
ring stand—2, and wire gauze
rubber stopper, 1-hole
salt solution (about 75 g NaCl in
    250 mL distilled H_2O
stoppers to fit flask and neck of
    condenser—2
thermometer, Celsius
watch glass—2

PREPARATION NOTES:

In this activity the student will learn how to separate a salt water mixture by distillation. Because of the large amount of equipment needed, it is highly recommended that this activity be done as a demonstration. Students will need help in understanding that the two solutions are different even though this is suggested by the watch glass data. This should be carefully emphasized in the post-lab discussion. **CAUTION:** Teacher should bend all pieces of glass tubing for students. All glass tubing, side arms and thermometers should be moistened with oil or glycerin before being inserted into rubber stoppers. Hold top of glass tube or thermometer with a rag or towel before inserting it with a twisting motion.

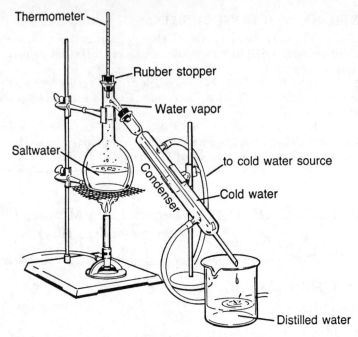

Thermometer

Rubber stopper

Water vapor

Saltwater

Condenser

to cold water source

Cold water

Distilled water

FIGURE 10-1

PROCEDURE:

1. Place 250 mL of a mixture of salt and water in 500 mL distilling flask with side arm. Place marble boiling chip in flask.
2. Fasten flask to ring stand with clamp.
3. Place wire gauze on ring and adjust ring so it is just underneath the flask.
4. Place thermometer into 1-hole rubber or cork stopper. See **CAUTION** above.
5. Place stopper with thermometer in top of flask.
6. Insert side arm into rubber stopper, lubricating first with oil or glycerin. Push side arm through 1-hole stopper until glass just appears on the other side.
7. Fit stopper into neck of condenser and fasten condenser to second ring stand with a clamp.
8. Attach rubber tubing to both ends of the water jack on the condenser. Attach the rubber tube connected to the bottom stem to the cold water source. Run other hose from top of condenser to sink.
9. Position beaker just below bottom of condenser.
10. Turn on water to condenser and check for leaks. The outer jacket of condenser should be cool.
11. Light the burner and warm the salt solution in the flask until it boils. Boil solution gently for 10 minutes.
12. Take a sample of liquid from flask and a sample of liquid from beaker and place each on a watch glass.
13. Evaporate to dryness over hot plate, water bath, or let air dry until next day.

ALTERNATE PROCEDURE:

(using more common laboratory equipment)

MATERIALS:

beaker	ring stand and ring
boiling chip	rubber stopper
Bunsen burner	rubber tubing, 30 cm
clamps—2	salt solution
Florence flask, 250 mL	test tube, 16 × 200 mm
glass tubing, 40 cm	source of water
glycerin	watch glass—2

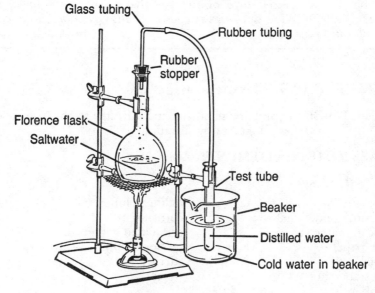

FIGURE 10-2

PREPARATION NOTES: See page 91.

PROCEDURE:

1. Place 125 mL of a salt solution in 250 mL Florence flask.
2. Make a right angle bend in piece of glass tubing halfway along the tube.
3. Insert one end of glass tubing into hole of rubber stopper, lubricating with oil or glycerin. Hold tubing with a rag or towel as it is inserted into stopper hole.
4. Insert the other end of glass tubing into rubber tubing.
5. Place open end of the rubber tube into test tube that is standing in a beaker of cold water.
6. Heat mixture in flask and allow it to boil gently for 10 minutes.
7. Take a sample of liquid from flask and a sample of liquid from test tube and place each on a watch glass.
8. Evaporate to dryness over hot plate, water bath, or let air dry until next day.

OBSERVATIONS AND DATA:

The salt solution boils and clear liquid drops appear at end of condenser and drop into beaker or test tube. The liquid from the beaker or test tube leaves no residue on the watch glass after it is evaporated. The liquid from the flask leaves a white residue when evaporated.

QUESTIONS AND CONCLUSIONS:

A mixture of salt and water can be separated by heating the solution. Heating causes the water to change into a gas. The gas cools and changes back into a liquid in the collecting vessel.

1. What two phase changes occur during distillation?   *evaporation and condensation*
2. What is left in the flask?   *salt and salt solution*
3. What is in the beaker or test tube?   *water only*
4. What is the temperature of the gas that passes into the condenser?   *100°C* What does this suggest?   *It suggests that water only has evaporated from the mixture.*

ACTIVITY 10-3: Mixtures (page 190)

OBJECTIVE: To prepare mixtures and investigate the separation of these mixtures by filtration

CLASS TIME ALLOTMENT: One period.

MATERIALS:

soil	iodine solution
jar, baby food, w/lid—3	cornstarch
clock or watch	graduated cylinder
filter paper	beaker, 100 mL
funnel	stirring rod
ring stand/ring	water
dropper	

PREPARATION NOTES:

In this activity the student prepares soil-water and cornstarch-water mixtures and investigates the separation of these mixtures by filtration. See Preparation of Solutions in Teacher's Guide for preparing iodine solution.

PROCEDURE:

1. Add 1 spoonful of soil to a small jar half full of water.
2. Tighten the lid and shake the jar vigorously.
3. Allow the jar to stand for 5 minutes. Observe the settling of the soil particles.
4. Pour half the liquid through a filter.
5. Describe the material in the filter and the liquid that has passed through. Observe the kind of mixture that is made by soil and water.
6. Add 1 drop of iodine solution to a jar containing 10 mL of water. Record your observations.
7. Put a very small amount of cornstarch in a clean jar containing 10 mL of water. Add 1 drop of iodine solution. Record your observations.
8. Put the same amount of cornstarch into a second clean jar containing 10 mL of water. Repeat steps 2-5. Describe the mixture before and after filtering.
9. Add 1 drop of iodine solution to the filtered liquid. Record your observations.

OBSERVATIONS AND DATA:

In Step 3 all the soil particles do not settle to the bottom. Some remain in solution. In Step 5 the material in the filter is soil particles. The muddy mixture is a suspension. It can be filtered. In step 7 the cornstarch solution turns blue-black when the iodine solution is added. In Step 8 the solution is cloudy before filtering and clearer after filtering. When a drop of iodine solution is added to the filtered liquid, the liquid turns blue-black. The change in color indicates that the cornstarch was not separated out.

QUESTIONS AND CONCLUSIONS:

There are many types of colloids. In this activity, the iodine test was used to detect the presence of starch (cornstarch) as evidence of the colloid mixture.

1. Where are the soil particles located after being allowed to settle for 5 minutes? *mostly on bottom of jar, but some suspended in water*
2. What kind of mixture is soil and water? How do you know? *suspension; it can be filtered*
3. What kind of mixture is cornstarch and water? *colloid; change in color of the iodine solution indicates that the cornstarch was not separated out*

ACTIVITY 10-4: Solubility (page 192)

OBJECTIVE: To compare the relative solubilities of sodium chloride, potassium nitrate, and boric acid.

CLASS TIME ALLOTMENT: 20 minutes

MATERIALS:

beakers, 100 mL (3)	salt
marking pencil	stirring rod
water, distilled	potassium nitrate
graduated cylinder	boric acid
balance	thermometer, Celsius

PREPARATION NOTES:

In this activity the student compares the relative solubilities of sodium chloride, potassium nitrate, and boric acid. Caution students to be careful when using thermometers to avoid breakage. Do not use thermometers to stir solutions. The point at which no more solvent will dissolve in the water is the point at which the solution is saturated.

PROCEDURE:

1. Label three beakers A, B, and C.
2. Pour 30 mL of distilled water into each beaker.
3. Measure and record the temperature of the water in each beaker.
4. Measure 2 g of table salt and add it to beaker A. Stir and record your observations.
5. Add more table salt, 2 g at a time until no more salt will dissolve. Be sure to stir after each addition of salt.
6. Record the total mass of salt that was added.

7. Repeat Steps 4 and 5 using potassium nitrate and beaker B.
8. Repeat Steps 4 and 5 using boric acid and beaker C.
9. Record all data.

OBSERVATIONS AND DATA:

BEAKER	WATER TEMPERATURE	SUBSTANCE ADDED	AMOUNT ADDED
A		table salt	
B		potassium nitrate	
C		boric acid	

Data will vary.

QUESTIONS AND CONCLUSIONS:

Different substances (solutes) have different solubilities in the solvent water. Temperature can also be a factor in solubility.
1. What was the solubility for each substance at the recorded temperature?
   Answers will vary
2. Which substance was most soluble?   *salt*
3. Which substance was least soluble?   *boric acid*

ADDITIONAL ACTIVITY: Which Substance is Most Soluble? (section 10:6)

OBJECTIVE: To compare the solubility of several substances and to observe the effect of a temperature change on solubility

CLASS TIME ALLOTMENT: One period.

MATERIALS:

beakers, 250 mL—4
beam balance
boric acid, 40 g
glass stirring rod
potassium nitrate, 40 g
ring stand/ring and wire gauze

source of heat
sugar, 40 g
table salt, 40 g
thermometer, -10°C to 110°C
water
marking pencil

PREPARATION NOTES:

In this activity the student compares the solubility of potassium nitrate, boric acid, sugar, and table salt and observes the effect of a temperature change on solubility. Generally, substances increase in solubility with an increase in temperature. However, salt has a solubility of 37 g/100 cm³ of water at 25°C and increases to only 40 g/100 cm³ at 100°C. Students will not likely see the additional 2 grams unless all the salt disappears. This will only happen if they have carefully measured the 40 grams. In some instances, solubility decreases with an increase in temperature, e.g., $Ce_2(SO_4)_3$ (cerium sulfate).

PROCEDURE:

1. Place 100 mL of water in each of four 250 mL beakers.
2. Record the temperature of the water in each beaker.

3. Place 40 g of table salt in the first beaker, 40 g of sugar in the second beaker, 40 g of boric acid in the third beaker, and 40 g of potassium nitrate in the fourth beaker. Label each beaker. Stir. How much of each substance dissolves? (little, most, etc.)
4. Heat the beaker containing potassium nitrate. Observe.
5. Cool the same beaker to 0°C with ice. Observe.
6. Repeat Steps 4 and 5 for the other three substances.

OBSERVATIONS AND DATA:

CHEMICAL DISSOLVED	AMOUNT ADDED	OBSERVATIONS AT ROOM TEMPERATURE	EFFECT OF HEATING
Table salt			
Sugar			
Boric acid			
Potassium nitrate			

A slight amount of boric acid dissolves. Most of the salt dissolves. All of the sugar dissolves. Most of the potassium nitrate dissolves and the solution becomes cold. Heating dissolves all of the chemical that was undissolved at room temperature.

QUESTIONS AND CONCLUSIONS:

1. How much of each substance dissolves at room temperature? *a little boric acid, most of the salt, most of the potassium nitrate, and all of the sugar dissolves*
2. Which solid is the most soluble in water at room temperature? *sugar*
3. Which solid is least soluble at room temperature? *boric acid*
4. How does solubility change with a decrease in temperature? *it decreases*
5. If the beaker that was heated were slowly cooled to room temperature, what kind of solution would result? *supersaturated*
6. When potassium nitrate is added to the beaker, what happens to the temperature? *decreases* How does this affect solubility as the crystal dissolves? *solubility also decreases*

ADDITIONAL ACTIVITY: Making a Supersaturated Solution (section 10:6)

OBJECTIVE: To make a supersaturated solution

CLASS TIME ALLOTMENT: One period.

MATERIALS:

beaker, 250 mL
graduated cylinder
heat source
ring stand/ring and wire gauze
stirring rod
table salt
water

PREPARATION NOTES:

In this activity the student makes a supersaturated salt solution. The final supersaturated solution will have only 3 grams more salt than at the beginning because the solubility of salt shows only a very slight increase with temperature. If you want to crystallize the 3 grams and demonstrate the excess, you will have a very difficult time.

PROCEDURE:

1. Place 100 mL of water, at room temperature, in a 250 mL beaker.
2. Slowly add table salt and stir until you reach the point at which no more salt dissolves. (This is critical. No more than a few pinches at a time should be added.)
3. Heat the solution to boiling.
4. Add more salt until it dissolves.
5. Slowly cool the solution to room temperature. Observe.

OBSERVATIONS AND DATA:

Salt dissolves until it reaches saturation point and then falls to the bottom of the beaker. If the temperature of the solution is raised, more salt will dissolve. If cooled slowly, the extra salt will remain in solution.

QUESTIONS AND CONCLUSIONS:

A supersaturated solution can be made by slowly cooling a saturated solution from its boiling temperature to room temperature.
1. What kind of solution is formed when the final salt solution is cooled to room temperature?   *supersaturated*
2. If the heated solution is cooled quickly, what will happen?   *extra solute will reappear as a solid at the bottom of the flask*
3. If all the salt dissolved at room temperature, what type of solution would result if the salt solution were heated?   *unsaturated, because the amount of salt needed for saturation when the solution is heated is increased*

ADDITIONAL ACTIVITY: Adding a Crystal to a Supersaturated Solution (section 10:6)

OBJECTIVE: To observe that the excess amount of solute can be recovered from a supersaturated solution

CLASS TIME ALLOTMENT: 30 minutes.

MATERIALS:

cotton
Erlenmeyer flask, 250 mL
heat source

hypo (hydrated sodium thiosulfate), 50 g
ring stand/ring and wire gauze
water

PREPARATION NOTES:

In this activity the student will dissolve and then recrystalize hypo to observe that the excess amount of a solute can be recovered from a supersaturated solution. You might have the better students do the experiment without the cotton plug. The cotton plug is added to prevent direct particles in the air from causing premature seeding as the solution cools.

PROCEDURE:
1. Place 100 mL of water in a 250 mL Erlenmeyer flask.
2. Place 50 g hypo into water. (Reserve one large crystal for Step 5.)
3. Heat until all hypo dissolves. Stopper flask with cotton.
4. Allow flask to slowly cool to room temperature.
5. Remove cotton and drop 1 large hypo crystal into solution. Observe.

OBSERVATIONS AND DATA:
The hypo dissolves when heated. When slowly cooled with cotton cover, no evidence of hypo is seen. Upon addition of extra hypo crystal, the crystal grows and a large amount of hypo forms.

QUESTIONS AND CONCLUSIONS:
The excess amount of solute present in a supersaturated solution can be removed by seeding the supersaturated solution with a large crystal of the solute.
1. What is the purpose of the cotton plug?   *to prevent dirt particles from seeding crystal formation*
2. What happens to temperature of water when hypo crystals are first added to 100 mL of water? Why?   *the temperature decreases, because the solute absorbs heat from its surroundings as it dissolves*
3. What happens to the volume of the solution when the hypo is dissolved? Why?   *the volume increases, because hypo contains trapped water that is released as crystals dissolve*

CHALLENGE: APPLYING SCIENTIFIC METHODS
Separating a Mixture by Distillation

OBJECTIVE: To physically separate a mixture by distillation

CLASS TIME ALLOTMENT: One period.

MATERIALS:
apron
copper sulfate solution, 40 mL
beaker, 400 mL
boiling chips (marble pieces)
buret clamp
burner
Erlenmeyer flask, 124 mL
glass bend
goggles
graduated cylinder, 50 mL
ice
matches

mineral oil
metric ruler
ring stand and ring
rubber stopper, 2-hole to fit 125 mL flask
rubber tubing, 30 cm
test tube rack
test tubes
thermometer, Celcius
watch glass
water
wire gauze

PREPARATION NOTES:

In this activity, the student sets up a distillation device to separate copper sulfate solution into its different parts. The student then compares the distillate to the original solution. To prepare copper sulfate, dissolve 159.6 g of copper sulfate in 1.0 L distilled water. Caution students to wear goggles and aprons while heating the mixture. Solution should be heated slowly. When inserting glass into the stopper, students should wrap both hands in cloth toweling. The ends of the tubing or thermometer to be inserted should be dipped in water or glycerin. Gently twist the tubing into the hole, never force it.

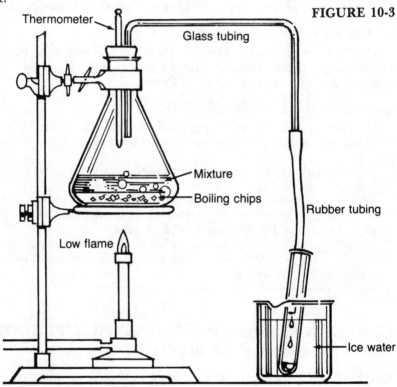

FIGURE 10-3

PROCEDURE:

1. Insert a 90° glass bend into one hole of the rubber stopper. CAUTION: Wet the end of the glass bend with water or glycerin. Wrap your hands in a cloth towel and gently twist the glass bend into the hole of the rubber stopper.
2. In the same manner, insert the thermometer through the other hole of the rubber stopper. Adjust the thermometer so the bulb is 10 cm below the rubber stopper.
3. Place the neck of the Erlenmeyer flask in the buret clamp and attach the clamp to the ring stand. The bottom of the flask should be resting on the wire gauze supported by the ring.
4. Pour 40 mL of the copper sulfate solution into the large test tube. Place two boiling chips into the mixture. Observe and record the color of the solution.
5. Place the rubber stopper apparatus on the Erlenmeyer flask.

6. Wet the end of the glass bend with mineral oil or glycerin. Attach rubber tubing to this end. Place the other end of the rubber tubing into a small test tube. The small test tube should be placed in a beaker that is half full of ice and water.
7. Gently heat the copper sulfate solution. CAUTION: Wear goggles and apron and heat gently. The mixture should not touch the thermometer bulb at any time. Only vapors will rise and touch the bulb.
8. When the mixture begins to boil, record the temperature. Continue to heat the solution until the temperature reaches 100°C. Collect a few milliliters of the distillate.
9. Turn off the burner. Remove the rubber tubing from the small test tube and remove the small test tube from the ice water.
10. Record the color of the liquid.

OBSERVATIONS AND DATA:

Student data will show slight variations. The mixture should appear blue, and the distillate colorless. The boiling point of the copper sulfate solution is 100°C.

QUESTIONS AND CONCLUSIONS:

1. What change occurs when the mixture boils?   *The liquid changes to a gas.*
2. How does liquid get into the small test tube placed in the beaker of ice water?   *The gas travels through the glass bend and rubber tubing into the test tube. It condenses into a liquid in the tube because of the cold temperature.*
3. (a) What liquid is in the small test tube?   *Probably water is in the small test tube.*
   (b) How could you identify this liquid?   *The density of the liquid could be calculated and compared to that of water.*
4. Is distillation using a physical change in the material or a chemical change in the material?   *Distillation uses a physical change in the material: namely a change of state.*

---

chapter 11

Elements

ADDITIONAL ACTIVITY: Metals and Nonmetals
(section 11:2)

OBJECTIVE: To identify metals and nonmetals by their physical properties

CLASS TIME ALLOTMENT: 20 minutes.

MATERIALS:

samples of the following elements:
aluminum   copper   lead   zinc
carbon   iron   sulfur

PREPARATION NOTES:

Be sure the metal samples are clean or students will not observe shininess, the property of luster.

PROCEDURE:

1. Obtain samples of the above elements. Clean each with sandpaper.
2. Study each sample and make a list of their physical properties: color, malleability, and luster. Determine whether a substance is brittle or malleable by considering what would happen if you hit the sample with a hammer. If it is brittle, the sample will crumble.
3. Classify each sample as a metal or nonmetal.
4. Classify each metal and nonmetal according to its position in the periodic table. Elements that would fall in the blue portion of Figure 11-3, page 203, are on the left side of the chart. Elements in the red portion would be considered to be on the right side of the chart.

OBSERVATIONS AND DATA:

	ALUMINUM	CARBON	COPPER	IRON	LEAD	SULFUR	ZINC
Color	Silvery	Black	Reddish	Black	Gray	Yellow	Gray
Malleable	Yes	No	Yes	Yes	Yes	No	Yes
Luster	Yes	Varies with sample	Yes	Yes	Yes	No	Yes

QUESTIONS AND CONCLUSIONS:

Metals are shiny and malleable; nonmetals have a dull finish and are brittle. Metals are found on the left side of the periodic table; nonmetals on the right side.

1. In what ways do these elements differ?   *Some are shiny; some are dull. Some are brittle; some are malleable.*
2. Which of the seven elements are metals? *aluminum, copper, zinc, lead, iron*
3. Which are nonmetals?   *sulfur, carbon*

ACTIVITY 11-1: Flame Tests (page 205)

OBJECTIVE: To test solutions of alkali metals and observe the characteristic test colors

CLASS TIME ALLOTMENT: 45 minutes.

MATERIALS: solutions of the following:

lithium chloride
potassium chloride
sodium chloride
cesium chloride
platinum or nichrome wire
hydrochloric acid (concentrated)

distilled water
burner
test tubes—5
test tube rack
beaker, 250 mL for distilled water
matches

CAUTION: Since concentrated hydrochloric acid produces the best results when cleaning the wire, the proper safety precautions must be taken. Students must wear goggles and clothing protection.

PREPARATION NOTES:

In this activity the student tests solutions of alkali metals and observes the characteristic flame test colors. Demonstrate the procedure for cleaning the nichrome wire by dipping it into hydrochloric acid and then into distilled water. Burn it in the flame until no color other than the flame is present. This procedure may have to be done several times to clean the wire from a previous sample. Show students how to adjust the burner so it burns with a blue flame. Use one of the four alkali metal salts listed above as the unknown metal. See Preparation of Solutions in Teacher's Guide for preparing salt solutions.

PROCEDURE:

1. Obtain chloride solutions of the following alkali metals: lithium, potassium, sodium cesium, and an unknown metal.
2. Clean a platinum or nichrome wire by dipping it into hydrochloric acid and then into distilled water. Dry the wire by heating it in the burner flame. Repeat this procedure until the wire no longer colors the burner flame.
3. Dip the clean wire into the lithium chloride solution.
4. Hold the wire at the tip of the inner cone of the burner flame. Record the color produced.
5. Clean the wire according to Step 2.
6. Repeat Steps 3-5 for each solution. Record the color for each compound.

OBSERVATIONS AND DATA:

SOLUTION	COLOR
lithium chloride	brilliant red
potassium chloride	violet
sodium chloride	yellowish orange
cesium chloride	violet
unknown	(depends on the one used)

QUESTIONS AND CONCLUSIONS:

Elements have characteristic colors. These colors can be used to identify some of the elements. Driftwood from the ocean will produce many of these colors when burned. The wood soaks up many different salts, and when dry, will burn with characteristic colors of such elements as magnesium, sodium, and potassium.

1. How can you be sure the chloride was not causing the color?   *The chlorine ion does not produce color.*
2. Why did you clean the wire between tests?   *to remove traces of previous test metals*
3. What was your unknown alkali metal? How do you know?   *Answers will vary.*

ACTIVITY 11-2: Transition Metals (page 208)

OBJECTIVE: To observe the colors of transition metal salts.

CLASS TIME ALLOTMENT: 30 minutes.

MATERIALS:

iron(II) sulfate   iron(II) chloride   copper(II) chloride
iron(III) sulfate   iron(III) chloride   copper(II) sulfate

PREPARATION NOTES:

In this activity students observe the colors of transition metal salts. Color can be used in some cases to identify compounds of these metals. Students shuld leave the containers sealed.

PROCEDURE:

Obtain samples of the following compounds: iron(II) sulfate, iron(III) sulfate, iron(II) chloride, iron(III) chloride, copper(II) chloride, and copper(II) sulfate. Record in a table the name and the color of each compound.

OBSERVATIONS AND DATA:

COMPOUND	COLOR
iron(II) sulfate	green
iron(III) chloride	yellow-brown
iron(II) chloride	green
iron(III) sulfate	yellow-brown
copper(II) chloride	blue
copper(II) sulfate	blue

QUESTIONS AND CONCLUSIONS:

1. What color do iron(II) compounds have? Iron(III) compounds? Copper(II) compounds?   *green; yellow-brown; blue*
2. What color would you predict for copper(II) nitrate? Why?   *blue, other copper(II) salts are blue.*
3. What color would you predict for iron(II) nitrate? Why?   *green, other iron(II) salts are green*

ADDITIONAL ACTIVITY: Properties of Carbon Dioxide (section 11:7)

OBJECTIVE: To observe the properties of carbon dioxide

CLASS TIME ALLOTMENT: One period.

MATERIALS:

candle   limestone or marble chips
gas bottle—2   rubber stopper, 2-hole, to fit gas bottle
glass plate, 6 cm x 6 cm   rubber tubing
glass tube, 90° bend   thistle tube or glass funnel
goggles   trough
hydrochloric acid, dilute   water

PREPARATION NOTES:

See Preparation of Solutions in Teacher's Guide for preparing dilute hydrochloric acid. **CAUTION:** Always add the acid to the water.

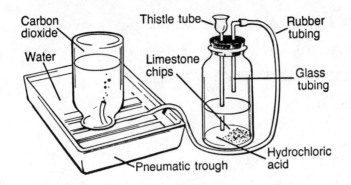

Carbon dioxide · Thistle tube · Rubber tubing · Water · Limestone chips · Glass tubing · Hydrochloric acid · Pneumatic trough

FIGURE 11-1

PROCEDURE:

1. Place limestone or marble chips in bottom of a gas bottle.
2. Place thistle tube and glass tubing in holes of rubber stopper. **CAUTION:** Moisten bottom ends of tubes with mineral oil or glycerin. Hold with a rag or towel and insert into stopper with a twisting motion.
3. Place stopper in top of gas bottle.
4. Attach one end of rubber tubing to glass tube.
5. Fill trough with water and position overflow spout so that any extra water will flow into the sink.
6. Fill the second gas bottle with water. Place glass plate over the top. Holding the plate with your hand, invert the bottle and place it in water trough in such a way that the bottle remains filled with water. Remove glass plate.
7. Insert free end of rubber tubing into bottom of inverted gas bottle.
8. Pour hydrochloric acid through thistle tube until bottom of thistle tube is covered with acid.
9. Collect gas in inverted gas bottle.
10. Test the collected gas by pouring gas over a burning candle.

OBSERVATIONS AND DATA:

The marble chips begin to bubble when the acid is poured on them. Bubbles pass through the water and collect at the top of the bottle. Water leaves the bottle since the gas does not dissolve in water. When the gas is poured on the flame, the flame goes out.

QUESTIONS AND CONCLUSIONS:

The gas produced does not dissolve in water, does not allow a candle to continue burning, and is heavier than air, indicating that the gas is carbon dioxide, as indicated by the equation:

$$CaCO_3 + HCl \longrightarrow CaCl_2 + H_2O + CO_2$$

1. Name the properties of carbon dioxide you discovered from this experiment. *does not dissolve in water, does not burn, is heavier than air so it sinks, is odorless*
2. What gas is formed when gasoline is burned in automobiles? *carbon monoxide*
3. Describe the properties of carbon monoxide. *odorless, colorless, combustible*

ACTIVITY 11-3: A Product of Burning (page 212)

OBJECTIVE: To observe the carbon produced from a burning candle

CLASS TIME ALLOTMENT: 20 minutes.

MATERIALS:

candle   glass square
matches   water

PREPARATION NOTES:

In this activity the student observes the carbon produced from burning a candle. Thus, the student sees that the candle wax is an organic compound. Point out that carbon dioxide and water are also formed when the candle burns. The soot formed is carbon.

PROCEDURE:

Light a candle and hold a cool glass square above it. **CAUTION:** Let the glass cool. Then, use cold water and try to wash the substance off the glass.

OBSERVATIONS AND DATA:

Students should observe that a black residue (carbon) forms on the glass. It cannot be washed off with water because it is an organic compound.

QUESTIONS AND CONCLUSIONS:

1. What happens when you hold a cool glass square above the candle?   *a black residue forms*
2. What happens when you try to wash the substance off the glass?   *it is insoluble*
3. Candles are made of wax that contains carbon. What substance formed on the glass?   *carbon (soot)*

ADDITIONAL QUESTIONS:

4. What else formed when the candle burned?   *carbon dioxide and water*
5. What is the candle made from? Is the compound organic or inorganic?   *wax, organic*
6. Why is the black residue insoluble in water?   *it is an organic compound*
7. What happens when a car burns gasoline containing carbon?   *the carbon particles are deposited on the inside of the engine*
8. How could the gasoline that is burned in a car contribute to air pollution?   *If too much carbon builds up it will enter the atmosphere from the exhaust gases.*

ADDITIONAL ACTIVITY: Preparing Oxygen Gas
(section 11:9)

OBJECTIVE: To prepare oxygen and observe its properties

CLASS TIME ALLOTMENT: One period.

MATERIALS:

Florence flask
funnel
gas bottles—2
glass plate, 6 cm × 6 cm
glass tube, 90° bend
goggles
graduated cylinder
glycerin
hydrogen peroxide (H_2O_2) 3%, 100 mL

manganese dioxide (MnO_2), 1 g
matches
ring stand and clamp
rubber stopper, 2-hole, to fit Florence flask
rubber tubing
towel
trough
water
wooden splint

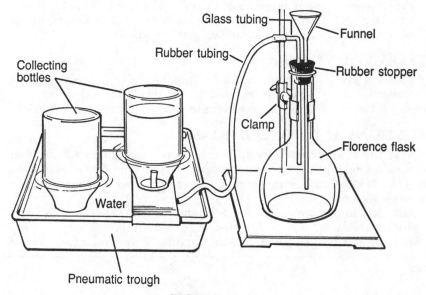

FIGURE 11-2

PREPARATION NOTES:

In this activity the student will prepare oxygen and observe its properties. This activity is suggested as a teacher demonstration. Before doing the activity, the teacher should demonstrate how to perform a splint test and what the characteristic test for oxygen is.

PROCEDURE:

1. Thoroughly wet a rubber stopper with water. Moisten ends of glass tube and funnel with glycerin. Holding tube and funnel with a towel, insert into rubber stopper with a twisting motion.
2. Attach a rubber tube to the glass bend after first wetting the glass bend.
3. Attach a Florence flask to ring stand clamp and fasten clamp to ring stand.
4. Fill a trough with water and position overflow spout so that any extra water will flow into sink.
5. Fill two gas bottles with water. Place glass plate over the top. Holding the plate with your hand, invert the bottles and place in water trough. Remove plate.

6. Place 1 g of MnO_2 in Florence flask.
7. Place rubber stopper with funnel and glass bend on top of the flask. Run the rubber tube so that the other end enters the bottom of one of the gas bottles.
8. Measure 100 mL H_2O_2 (3%) in graduated cylinder. Pour 25 mL into funnel. NOTE: Small amount of H_2O_2 will be trapped in funnel. This keeps the gas formed from flowing out through funnel.
9. When bubbling in gas bottle subsides, add another 25 mL H_2O_2 (3%). When one gas bottle becomes empty, move the rubber tube to the next bottle.
10. Test the gas in each bottle by lighting a wooden splint and blowing the flame out, leaving the end glowing. Insert the end that is glowing into the bottom of each bottle. Record observations. NOTE: This is a standard test for oxygen. The splint will burst into flames with a popping noise when it is in contact with oxygen.

OBSERVATIONS AND DATA:

Bubbles of gas flow through the water from the end of the rubber tubing and collect at the top of the inverted bottle, displacing the water. The glowing splint bursts into flame when the splint is lowered into bottle.

QUESTIONS AND CONCLUSIONS:

Oxygen can be prepared by adding hydrogen peroxide to manganese dioxide. It is lighter than air and is necessary for burning. Since the glowing splint bursts into flames with a popping noise when lowered into the bottle, the gas is oxygen.
1. What do you observe when the gas given off in the experiment is tested with a glowing splint?   *The glowing splint bursts into flames.*
2. What gas was formed when the MnO_2 and H_2O_2 were mixed?   *oxygen*

ACTIVITY 11-4: Identifying Sulfides (page 214)

OBJECTIVE: To identify certain metals by the color of their sulfides

CLASS TIME ALLOTMENT: One period.

MATERIALS:

graduated cylinder	marking pencil
lead nitrate solution	paper
zinc sulfate solution	tape
bismuth nitrate solution	test tube rack
antimony(III) chloride solution	dropper
hydrogen sulfide solution	test tubes—4

PREPARATION NOTES:

In this activity the student identifies certain metals by the color of their sulfides. Demonstrate the use of the hydrogen sulfide solution before students begin to work. After students complete the exercise, have them make a chart in their notebooks that lists the sulfides, their formulas, and the color of each. See Preparation of Solutions in Teacher's Guide for preparing salts and hydrogen sulfide.

PROCEDURE:

1. Pour 5 mL of each of the following solutions into separate test tubes: lead nitrate, zinc sulfate, bismuth nitrate and antimony(III) chloride.
2. Label each test tube with the name of the compound.
3. Cover the labels with a piece of paper.
4. Have someone rearrange the test tubes in the rack.
5. Add 5 drops of hydrogen sulfide solution to each test tube. Record the color. **CAUTION:** Hyrdogen sulfide may cause burns. Avoid spillage. Rinse all spills with water.
6. Lead sulfide is black; zinc sulfide is white; bismuth sulfide is brown, and antimony(III) sulfide is orange. Determine which metal is present in each test tube. Uncover the labels and check your results.

OBSERVATIONS AND DATA:

Students should observe the following: Antimony sulfide is orange; bismuth sulfide is brown; lead sulfide is black; and zinc sulfide is white. Have students uncover the labels to check their results.

QUESTIONS AND CONCLUSIONS:

1. What did you use to identify the metal in the sulfides?   *the color of the metallic sulfide*
2. Each time you added a few drops of hydrogen sulfide to the test tubes a color change occurred. Why did this change happen?   *A chemical reaction occurred. Sulfur combined with the metal in each test tube.*

ADDITIONAL ACTIVITY: Chlorine Bleaches (section 11:10)

OBJECTIVE: To see the effect of chlorine bleach on different materials

CLASS TIME ALLOTMENT: 15 minutes on three different days.

MATERIALS:

beaker, 250 mL	liquid bleach, 200 mL
cotton cloth sample, bright colored	wool cloth sample
goggles	

PREPARATION NOTES:

In this activity the student will see the effect of chlorine bleach on different materials. **CAUTION:** Students should be very careful not to splash bleach in their eyes and to avoid getting bleach on their clothes.

PROCEDURE:

1. Place a piece of bright colored cloth in a 250 mL beaker. Add 100 mL liquid bleach.
2. Let the beaker stand for 24 hours. Observe.
3. In a second beaker, place a piece of wool and 100 mL of bleach.
4. Let the beaker stand for two days. Observe.
5. Rinse the cloth with water. Attempt to stretch and tear the cotton and wool.
6. Compare the strength with the original cotton and wool cloth.

OBSERVATIONS AND DATA:

Color will probably disappear from cotton sample. (This will vary depending upon particular dyes present. Some dyes are more resistant than others to the bleaching.) The color will fade from the woolen sample. The cotton can be stretched more after bleaching. The wool fabric seems to lose its structure, therefore its strength.

QUESTIONS AND CONCLUSIONS:

Beach will remove the color from most cotton fabrics. Bleach has less effect on colors in wool. Bleach will cause wool to lose its texture and structure. It is the chlorine in the bleach that is responsible for these effects.
1. What is the chemical formula for bleach?   *NaOC1*
2. What element causes some fabrics to lose color?   *chlorine*

CHALLENGE: APPLYING SCIENTIFIC METHODS
Properties of Iodine and the Iodide Ion

OBJECTIVE: To investigate the differences in properties of iodine and the iodide ion

CLASS TIME ALLOTMENT: One period.

MATERIALS:

apron	paper
beaker, 100 mL	potassium iodide, 3 crystals
bleach, 3 mL	ring stand and ring
burner	tincture of iodine
evaporating dish, 20 mL	vinegar, 10 mL
goggles	water
ice	wire gauze
matches	

PREPARATION NOTES:

In this activity the student compares the properties of the free iodine with the iodide molecule. Free iodine (I_2) exists as a solid, which, when heated, sublimes to a violet vapor. Iodine also exists as an ion, I^-, in compounds called iodides. Students perform the starch test for iodine and potassium iodide, and release iodine from potassium iodide by reacting the potassium iodide with vinegar and bleach. Caution students to wear their goggles and aprons. This activity should be performed in a well ventilated room. Caution students not to inhale vapors. Bleach and iodine can cause burns. Rinse all spills with water. You may wish to perform steps 6 through 9 as a demonstration.

PROCEDURE:

1. Place a drop of tincture of iodine on a piece of paper. Record your observations. NOTE: Paper contains starch.
2. Make a solution of potassium iodide. First put two large crystals of potassium iodide in a beaker. Add 20 mL water and stir until the crystals dissolve.

3. Place a drop of potassium iodide solution on the paper. Observe and record your observations.
4. Add 2 to 3 mL bleach to the potassium iodide solution in the beaker. Place a drop of this new solution on the paper. Observe and record the results.
5. Add 10 mL vinegar to the above solution. Place a drop of this solution on the paper. Observe and record your results.
6. Place a beaker with the solution from Step 5 on a wire gauze that is attached to a ring stand. Place an evaporating dish on top of the beaker. Put 3 cubes of ice in the dish.
7. Gently heat the solution under a fume hood or in a well ventilated area. Observe and record any changes. **CAUTION:** Wear goggles and apron. Do not breathe fumes.
8. Continue to heat the beaker for about 10 minutes until gray crystals (iodine) form on the bottom of the evaporating dish.
9. Remove the burner and allow to cool. When evaporating dish is cool, your teacher will scrape the crystals onto a piece of notebook paper. Observe and record what happens to the paper. **CAUTION:** Avoid touching iodine crystals.

OBSERVATIONS AND DATA:

A red-orange color forms in the heated solutions of potassium iodide, bleach, and vinegar. The solution turns to a violet vapor when heated. Gray-silver colored crystals form on the bottom of the evaporating dish as heating continues. Tincture of iodine, potassium iodide solution plus bleach and vinegar, and iodine crystals turn the paper black or blue-black. There is no color change when potassium iodide or potassium iodide solution plus bleach is added to paper.

QUESTIONS AND CONCLUSIONS:

1. Why did the paper turn blue-black when the tincture of iodine was placed on it? Iodine in the presence of starch turns blue-black.   *Because the paper contains starch, the starch reacted with the iodine to cause the blue-black color.*
2. How do you know that iodide is not the same as iodine?   *The iodide ion did not give the same color reaction to starch as did the iodine.*
3. (a) What was formed when bleach and vinegar were added to the potassium iodide solution?   *Iodine was formed.*
   (b) How do you know?   *The paper turned black, which is similar to the reaction of iodine and paper.*
4. (a) What color did the paper turn when the crystals were placed on it.   *Blue-black*
   (b) Why?   *The starch in the paper reacted with the iodine to cause the blue-black color.*

---

chapter 12

Reactions

ADDITIONAL ACTIVITY: Ions (section 12:1)

OBJECTIVE: To determine if ions conduct electricity

CLASS TIME ALLOTMENT: 25 minutes.

MATERIALS:

beaker	salt
bell wire, insulated, 1 m	sugar
dry cells, 1.5 volt—2	water, distilled
flashlight bulb (microlamp), 3 volt	wire cutters or tool to strip insulation from wire

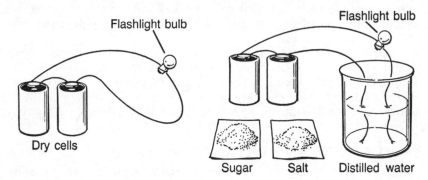

FIGURE 12-1

PREPARATION NOTES:

In this activity, students determine if ions can conduct electricity. Have paper towels or cloth towels available to dry the ends of the wires. You may wish to present this activity to the class as a demonstration.

PROCEDURE:

1. Strip 1 cm of insulation from the ends of 3 pieces of bell wire.
2. Connect the wires to the batteries and bulb as pictured in the figure above.
3. Cut one wire in the circuit. Remove about 1 cm of insulation from cut ends.
4. Place two bare ends of wire into a beaker half full of distilled water. Observe if the light is glowing.
5. Dry the cut ends of the wire. Place them into a pile of dry salt. Observe the bulb.
6. Sprinkle a few grams of sugar into the water. Using clean ends of the wire, place the cut ends into the sugar and water. Observe the bulb.
7. Repeat using fresh distilled water and table salt. Record observations.

OBSERVATIONS AND DATA:

The bulb lights only when the cut ends of the wire are in the beaker containing salt and water.

QUESTIONS AND CONCLUSIONS:

Salt breaks up into ions only when in solution and the ions then provide a pathway for electricity to flow the solution. Pure water or a solution of pure water and sugar do not form or contain ions since the bulb does not light.
1. Does the bulb light with only water?   *no*

2. Does the bulb light when sugar is added to the water? *no*
3. Do you think sugar adds ions to the water? Why? *No, if ions were present, electricity would have been conducted to the bulb.*
4. Does the table salt add ions to water? Explain. *Yes, ions must be present since the electricity flowed from one part of the liquid to another and flowed to the bulb. The ions could only have come from the salt. Water alone did not conduct electricity.*

ADDITIONAL ACTIVITY: Acids Cause Color Changes (section 12:7)

OBJECTIVE: To see the effect of acids on dyes present in foods

CLASS TIME ALLOTMENT: 15 minutes.

MATERIALS:

baking soda   red cabbage or beets
eye droppers—4   rubbing alcohol
glass jar with screw cap   vinegar

PREPARATION NOTES:

In this activity the student will observe the effect of acids and bases on dyes present in foods. The amount of vinegar needed to turn the purple alcohol solution to a red color is less than the amount needed to turn the solution red when it is a green color.

PROCEDURE:

1. Shred some red cabbage into a glass jar.
2. Add some rubbing alcohol and put the lid on the jar.
3. Shake container until the alcohol turns purple.
4. Add some vinegar to the solution a drop at a time. Record when a color change occurs.
5. Add pinches of baking soda until the solution becomes green.
6. Add vinegar again. Observe the results.

OBSERVATIONS AND DATA:

Adding vinegar initially to the purple cabbage-alcohol solution produces a red color. Adding pinches of baking soda changes the red to green. Another addition of vinegar to this solution will return the red color.

QUESTIONS AND CONCLUSIONS:

The vinegar is acting as an acid; the baking soda as a base. The dye in the cabbage is responding to the presence of the acid and base. The color change can be used as a test (in indicator) for acid.

1. Which element in the vinegar is responsible for the color change? *hydrogen*
2. What did the pinch of baking soda do to the vinegar? *It neutralized it.*
3. What acid does vinegar contain? *acetic acid*
4. What is the function of baking soda? *acts as a base*

ACTIVITY 12-1: Acids and Bases (page 240)

OBJECTIVE: To use litmus in testing acids and bases

CLASS TIME ALLOTMENT: 20 minutes first day, 10 minutes second day.

MATERIALS:

jars, baby food—4
marking pencil
graduated cylinder, 100 mL
buttermilk
milk of magnesia
water, distilled

litmus paper
beakers, 400 mL—2
ammonia
vinegar
balance
petroleum jelly

PREPARATION NOTES:

In this activity the student uses litmus in testing acids and bases and observes the effect of a base on petroleum jelly. Litmus paper turns red in acids and blue in bases. Grease such as petroleum jelly will form a colloidal mixture with a base such as ammonia.

PROCEDURE:

1. Label 4 small jars A, B, C, and D.
2. Pour 25 mL buttermilk into jar A. Pour 25 mL vinegar into jar B. Pour 25 mL milk of magnesia into jar C. Pour 25 mL distilled water into jar D.
3. Use litmus paper to test for acids and bases.
4. Label 2 beakers E and F.
5. Pour 100 mL distilled water into each beaker.
6. Add 40 mL of ammonia solution to beaker E.
7. Add 40 mL of vinegar to beaker F.
8. Add about 2 g petroleum jelly to each beaker. Allow the beakers to stand undisturbed overnight.
9. Observe the contents of each beaker and record your observations.

OBSERVATIONS AND DATA:

TEST TUBE	CONTENTS	LITMUS TEST	ACID OR BASE
A	buttermilk	red	acid
B	vinegar	red	acid
C	milk of magnesia	blue	base
D	distilled water	no color change	neither (control)

Beakers after standing overnight:

BEAKER	CONTENTS	OBSERVATIONS
E	ammonia and petroleum jelly	petroleum jelly dissolved
F	vinegar and petroleum jelly	no change

QUESTIONS AND CONCLUSIONS:

Litmus paper turns red in acids and blue in bases. Grease such as petroleum jelly will form a colloidal mixture with a base such as ammonia. This explains the action of ammonia to dissolve grease when used in a window cleaner.

1. What happens to the petroleum jelly?   *It dissolves in the ammonia and does not dissolve in the vinegar.*
2. What is used to clean grease off the surface of walls?   *ammonia*

ACTIVITY 12-2: pH Values (page 240)

OBJECTIVE: To determine the pH of selected solutions

CLASS TIME ALLOTMENT: 20 minutes.

MATERIALS:

graduated cylinder	apple juice	corn syrup
test tubes—11	orange juice	salt water
pH paper	sauerkraut juice	milk of magnesia
lemon juice	tomato juice	shampoo
ginger ale	milk	

PREPARATION NOTES:

In this activity the student tests selected solutions to determine the pH of each. Demonstrate the procedure for testing with pH paper.

PROCEDURE:

1. Obtain 10-mL samples of each of the following substances: lemon juice; ginger ale; apple juice; orange juice; sauerkraut juice, tomato juice; milk; corn syrup; salt water; milk of magnesia; and shampoo.
2. Use a separate piece of pH paper for each sample and determine the pH value of each. Record all values.
3. Rank the substance in order of pH values from the lowest to the highest.

OBSERVATIONS AND DATA:

SUBSTANCE	pH	RANK	pH
lemon juice	2.3	lemon juice	2.3
ginger ale	2.5	ginger ale	2.5
apple juice	3.0	apple juice	3.0
orange juice	3.5	orange juice	3.5
sauerkraut juice	3.5	sauerkraut juice	3.5
tomato juice	4.2	tomato juice	4.2
milk	6.5	shampoo	5.3
corn syrup	6.7	milk	6.5
salt water	about 8.4	corn syrup	6.7
milk of magnesia	10.4	salt water	8.4
shampoo	5.3 *varies*	milk of magnesia	10.4

QUESTIONS AND CONCLUSIONS:

1. Which substance tested has the lowest pH?   *lemon juice*
2. Which has the highest pH?   *milk of magnesia*
3. Classify your samples as acids, bases, or neutral substances.   *Acids: lemon juice, orange juice, ginger ale, apple juice, sauerkraut juice, tomato juice, shampoo. Bases: milk of magnesia, milk, corn syrup, salt water. Neutral: none are truly neutral.*

ACTIVITY 12-3: Neutralization (page 241)

OBJECTIVE: To investigate the neutralization of vinegar by ammonia water

CLASS TIME ALLOTMENT: One period.

MATERIALS:

beaker, 100 mL	vinegar
dropper	graduated cylinder, 100 mL
phenolphthalein	ammonia
water, distilled	

PREPARATION NOTES:

In this activity the student investigates the neutralization of vinegar by ammonia water. The solution at the start is acidic. As ammonia (base) is added, the acid is neutralized and the change in color of the phenolphthalein from clear to pink indicates the shift from acidic to basic. The reaction between acetic acid in the vinegar and the ammonia produces ammonium acetate and water.

PROCEDURE:

1. Add 5 drops of phenolphthalein to 50 mL of water in a beaker.
2. Add 10 mL of vinegar to the beaker. Observe whether the solution is an acid or base.
3. To the same beaker, add ammonia water, one drop at a time, until a color change occurs.

OBSERVATIONS AND DATA:

Students should observe that the solution at the beginning of the experiment was clear and therefore an acid. When ammonia was added, the color changed to pink, thus making it a base.

QUESTIONS AND CONCLUSIONS:

1. Is the vinegar solution an acid or base? How do you know?   *acid solution—clear*
2. After adding ammonia water, is the solution an acid or base? How do you know?   *base—color change of clear to pink*
3. Was the pH of the solution above 7 or below 7 before you added the final drop?   *less below 7*
4. How does this activity relate to neutralization?   *The solution at the start is an acid. As a base is added, it becomes neutral and as more base is added, finally becomes a base. The properties of both the acid and base are changed in this activity. As the point the pH reaches 7, neutralization has been completed and a salt water*

solution results. If you continue to add ammonia water, you would add enough hydroxide ions to create a base solution.
5. What is phenolphthalein?   *an indicator*

CHALLENGE: APPLYING SCIENTIFIC METHODS
Generating a Gas

OBJECTIVE: To produce hydrogen gas from an acid and determine some of the properties of hydrogen gas

CLASS TIME ALLOTMENT: One period.

MATERIALS:

apron	rubber stopper, #4, 1-hole
bucket, plastic	rubber tubing, 25 cm
buret clamp	test tube, large
glass bend, 90°	test tube, small, 4
goggles	test tube rack
hydrochloric acid	towel
matches	wooden splint, 4
rubber stopper, #2, solid, 4	zinc, mossy, 3 g

PREPARATION NOTES:

In this activity, students determine how hydrogen gas is obtained from an acid. For example, in the equation $Zn + 2HCl \longrightarrow ZnCl_2 + H_2$, the action of zinc will remove the hydrogen from the hydrochloric acid. Students then determine the properties of color, odor, density, and flammability of hydrogen gas. To prepare 6 M HCl, slowly add 100.0 mL hydrochloric acid to 100.0 mL distilled water. Caution students to wear goggles and aprons. Acids may cause burns. If acid spills, wash area with water.

PROCEDURE:

1. Insert a glass bend into a rubber stopper that has been wet with water. **CAUTION:** Use towel to wrap the glass bend. Gently twist the glass bend as you insert it into the stopper.
2. Fasten the rubber tubing to the glass bend.
3. Place a large test tube in the buret clamp. Attach the clamp to a ring stand. Attach the rubber stopper assembly to the top of the test tube.
4. Fill a plastic bucket ½ full of water. Fill 4 small test tubes with water. Place the test tubes in a test tube rack.
5. Remove the rubber stopper assembly. **CAUTION:** Wear goggles and apron. Place about 3 g mossy zinc (2 pieces) and 15 mL hydrochloric acid in the test tube. Quickly close the test tube with the rubber stopper assembly.
6. Invert the test tubes in the bucket, one at a time. Collect the hydrogen gas that comes off by placing the rubber tube in the test tubes. Keep the rubber tube in a test tube until the water completely runs out. Seal each test tube with a rubber stopper after it is filled with gas and replace it in the test tube rack. If bubbles stop before the test tubes are full, add more zinc or acid to the large test tube.
7. After you have collected 4 test tubes of gas, leave the rubber tubing in the bucket until the bubbling stops.

8. Record the color of the gas collected. Record the odor by gently waving air above an unstoppered test tube toward your nose.
9. NOTE: For Steps 9 and 10 students should work in pairs. Student A should hold a lighted wooden splint. Student B should unstopper a test tube and hold it upside down. Then Student A should put the lighted splint into the mouth of the test tube. Record your observations.
10. Take the third and fourth test tubes and hold them side by side. Invert one and remove the rubber stoppers from both. Wait 60 seconds. Repeat the lighted splint test for each test tube. Record your observation.

OBSERVATIONS AND DATA:

Hydrogen gas is colorless and odorless. It has a high flammability, as evidenced by the pop that sounded when the lighted splint was inserted into a tube of gas. Hydrogen gas is lighter than air.

QUESTIONS AND CONCLUSIONS:

1. (a) Would you consider the gas to be dangerous if the flaming splint popped when placed in a test tube of gas?   *yes*
   (b) Why?   *The popping sound indicates that the gas burns very rapidly.*
2. (a) A gas pushes water out of a test tube when it is bubbled through it. Does this mean that the gas is soluble or insoluble in water?   *This means that the gas is insoluble in water.*
   (b) Explain.   *If the gas were soluble in water, it would not displace the water to form bubbles, but would dissolve.*
3. (a) Does the test tube that is upside down in Step 10 have hydrogen in it after 60 seconds?   *Yes*
   (b) How do you know?   *The burning splint pops when it is held to the test tube. The pop indicates that hydrogen is present.*
4. (a) Suppose the flame test for hydrogen was positve in the test tube that is right side up after 60 seconds. Would the density of the gas be greater than, less than, or the same as air?   *The density would be greater than air.*
   (b) Explain.   *In order for the gas to stay in a test tube right side up, it would be displaced by air in the test tube.*
5. Is the reaction $Zn + 2HCl \longrightarrow ZnCl_2 + H_2$ a synthesis reaction or a single displacement reaction.   *This reaction is a single displacement reaction.*
6. Write the equation for this reaction if magnesium metal had been used instead of the zinc.   *$Mg + 2HCl \longrightarrow MgCl_2 + H_2$*

---

chapter 13

Chemical Technology

ACTIVITY 13-1: Plastics (page 252)

OBJECTIVE: To classify plastic items as thermosetting plastics or thermoplastics

CLASS TIME ALLOTMENT: 10 minutes.

MATERIALS:

PREPARATION NOTES:

In this activity students survey their homes to make lists of plastic items. They then classify these items as thermosetting or thermoplastic.

PROCEDURE:

Make a list of 10 items in your home that are made of plastic. Use Table 13-2 to determine if each plastic is a thermoplastic or a thermosetting plastic.

OBSERVATIONS AND DATA:

Lists will probably show more thermoplastic items.

QUESTIONS AND CONCLUSIONS:

1. Were most of the plastics thermoplastics?   *Answers will vary.*
2. Why do you think these items were made of plastic.   *to substitute for wood, glass, or metal*
3. What properties does each plastic have that make it suitable for that item?   *The properties of plastics (strong, lightweight, resilient, easily molded, inexpensively produced) make them suitable for a variety of uses. Answers will vary.*
4. Of what natural substance could each item be made?   *Answers will vary. Possible responses are: aluminum foil could be used instead of plastic wrap; wool carpet could be used instead of nylon; containers could be made of glass or metal.*

ADDITIONAL ACTIVITY: Making a Polymerlike Substance (section 13:5)

OBJECTIVE: To prepare and examine a substance that acts like a polymer

CLASS TIME ALLOTMENT: 20 minutes.

MATERIALS:

beaker, 400 mL
bowl, plastic
corn starch—250 g (about ½ box of regular cornstarch)
stirring device
water

PREPARATION NOTES:

You might want groups of four to perform the experiment to cut down on the clean-up. About 50 mL more water may be needed in making the cornstarch paste.

PROCEDURE:

1. Mix about 250 g of cornstarch with 125 mL of water. Add additional water if any powder is left.

2. Make a thick paste from the above.
3. With your palm quickly push on the surface of the paste. Observe.
4. Put your finger in the paste slowly. Slowly pull it out. Observe.

OBSERVATIONS AND DATA:

The pastelike substance regains its shape when a hand breaks the surface. The substance seems to be one continuous cluster of particles.

QUESTIONS AND CONCLUSIONS:

This substance is like a polymer. It is elastic in texture and feels like a continuous strand of material with no natural break in it.
1. How does the substance react when a hand is placed on the surface? *An impression is made in the substance, but slowly disappears on settling.*
2. How does the substance react when your finger is put into the paste? *The hole that is created is quickly closed up.*
3. Explain how this paste is like a polymer, such as synthetic rubber. *It forms a long continuous substance with a shiny, plastic-looking surface. It keeps its shape when deformed, which is characteristic of a softer texture plastic.*

ACTIVITY 13-2: Synthetic Fibers (page 254)

OBJECTIVE: To determine the properties of synthetic fibers and contrast these with the properties of natural fibers

CLASS TIME ALLOTMENT: One period.

MATERIALS:

beakers, 250 mL—6	fabric samples, red (15 cm x 15 cm)
hair dryer	nylon
laundry marker	polyester
paper towels	acrylic
chlorine bleach	cotton
water	wool
watch or clock	cotton-polyester blend

PREPARATION NOTES:

In this activity students determine the properties of selected synthetic fibers. These properties are then compared to those of natural fibers. Be certain to use a laundry marker with insoluble ink. Demonstrate the use of the hair dryer to dry a fabric sample. Caution students in using the bleach not to get any on their hands or clothing. Students should rinse away with water any bleach that spills accidentally. Direct students to make a table similar to the one shown on page 254 and to record their data in this table.

PROCEDURE:

1. Using the laundry marker, label each sample with fabric type.
2. Soak the nylon sample in water for 3 minutes. Remove this sample and place it on a paper towel.
3. Dry the sample with the hair dryer. Record the time it takes to dry.

4. Take the nylon sample and wad it into a ball. Hold the ball for 1 minute and then open the sample. Record the appearance of the sample.
5. Try to remove 1 thread from the side of the nylon sample. Record whether or not it ravels easily, as well as the appearance of the sample after the thread is removed.
6. Try to tear the nylon sample. Record the results.
7. Place the nylon sample in a beaker and cover it with chlorine bleach. Let the beaker stand overnight.
8. Repeat Steps 2-7 with the other fabric samples.
9. The next day, observe the bleached fabric samples and record your observations.

OBSERVATIONS AND DATA:

FABRIC SAMPLE	DRYING TIME (MIN)	WRINKLES	RAVELS	TEARS	BLEACH EFFECTS

QUESTIONS AND CONCLUSIONS:

1. Which of the samples are synthetic?   *polyester, acrylic, nylon*   Which are natural?   *cotton, wool*
2. What are the differences between the properties of synthetic and natural fibers?   *Natural fibers take longer to dry, wrinkle more easily, and are less resistant to wear and chemicals.*
3. What do you think are the advantages of blended fibers over pure fibers?   *wear resistant, resistant to stains, resistant to wrinkling when washed; blended fabrics can have all the good properties of synthetic and natural fibers.*

ADDITIONAL ACTIVITY: Making Soap (section 13:6)

OBJECTIVE: To make soap from household products

CLASS TIME ALLOTMENT: one class period

MATERIALS:
beam balance
beaker, 400 mL
goggles
heat source
heat stand
lard—30 g
lye, 20%, 100 mL
table salt (NaCl)—5 g

PREPARATION NOTES:

See Preparation of Solutions for preparation of lye solution. Make the solution before the activity starts. **CAUTION:** Lye is a caustic substance. Students must wear goggles when working with it. Rinse with large amounts of water if lye splashes on clothes or body.

PROCEDURE:
1. Place 30 g lard in beaker.
2. Add 100 mL of 20% lye solution. **CAUTION:** Wear goggles. Lye is a caustic substance. Rinse with large amounts of water if lye splashes on clothes or body.
3. Boil gently for 15 minutes.
4. Let mixture stand a few minutes and then add 5 g table salt.
5. Skim soap off top of water, press into a cake, let dry.
6. Find the mass of the dry soap.
7. Place small amount of soap into test tube ¼ full of water. Shake.

OBSERVATIONS AND DATA:
The soap forms after the lye and lard are heated. The mass of the dried soap is less than the mass of the lard and lye used.

QUESTIONS AND CONCLUSIONS:
Soap can be made from the addition of a fat substance and sodium hydroxide.
1. Account for any difference in mass. *According to the equation, fat + lye ⟶ glycerol + soap, glycerol is also produced. This accounts for the difference in mass between end products and beginning substance.*

ADDITIONAL ACTIVITY: Comparing Cleaning Actions (section 13:6)

OBJECTIVE: To compare the sudsing action of soap and detergent in soft and hard water

CLASS TIME ALLOTMENT: 15 minutes.

MATERIALS:
hard water
liquid soap
soft water
synthetic detergent
test tubes, 16 x 150 cm—2

PREPARATION NOTES:
Liquid soap may be made by dissolving soap flakes in distilled water. Synthetic detergent may be any dishwashing powder not mentioned under soaps.

PROCEDURE:
1. Obtain two test tubes and fill each one-half full of soft water.
2. Add 1 drop of liquid soap to one test tube and one drop of liquid detergent to the other test tube. Shake. Observe.
3. Repeat Steps 1 and 2 using hard water. Observe.

OBSERVATIONS AND DATA:
The amount of sudsing is the same with the soap and detergent in soft water. In hard water, the amount of sudsing is the same as with soft water for the detergent, but considerably less for the liquid soap.

QUESTIONS AND CONCLUSIONS:

1. What is the control in this experiment?   *the test tubes of liquid soap and detergent in soft water*
2. Why is soap better to use if soft water is available?   *There is less sudsing and it can be purified from waste water easier than some detergents. Detergents can promote algae growth and the resultant loss of oxygen to water life.*
3. If someone had hard water at home and wanted to use soap as a washing agent, what could be done?   *Washing soda could be used with soap to effectively soften the water.*

ACTIVITY 13-3: Precipitation (page 258)

OBJECTIVE: To prepare a precipitate of aluminum hydroxide

CLASS TIME ALLOTMENT: 20 minutes

MATERIALS:

aluminum chloride, 20 g   sodium hydroxide, dilute
beakers, 250 mL—2   balance
filter paper   stirring rod
funnel   water, distilled
ring stand and ring   graduated cylinder, 100 mL

PREPARATION NOTES:

In this activity the student prepares a precipitate of aluminum hydroxide. This substance is used to trap sediment in the water purification process. See Preparation of Solutions in Teacher's Guide for preparing dilute NaOH solution.

PROCEDURE:

1. Moisten a piece of filter paper with water and put it in a supported funnel.
2. Dissolve 20 g aluminum chloride ($AlCl_3$) in 100 mL water in a beaker.
3. Slowly add 10 mL dilute sodium hydroxide (NaOH) solution.
4. Pour the solution through the filter into another beaker.

OBSERVATIONS AND DATA:

A white gel-like precipitate forms when the two chemicals are mixed. This precipitate is trapped in the filtering paper during the filtering process.

QUESTIONS AND CONCLUSIONS:

When aluminum chloride is added to sodium hydroxide, a precipitate of aluminum hydroxide is formed.
1. What is the material in the filter?   *aluminum hydroxide*
2. Write a chemical equation for the reaction that took place.
$$AlCl_3 + 3NaOH \longrightarrow Al(OH)_3 \uparrow + 3NaCl$$

ADDITIONAL ACTIVITY: Filtering Muddy Water (section 13:7)

OBJECTIVE: To design and use a filtration tower

CLASS TIME ALLOTMENT: One period.

MATERIALS:

beaker, 250 mL
glass cylinder, open-end, 5 cm
diameter, 20-30 cm long
glass tube, 6 mm diameter, 15 cm
long
gravel, fine and coarse

muddy water
rubber stopper, 1-hole, 5 cm diameter
sand

PREPARATION NOTES:

Moisten end of glass tube with glycerin and use a towel when inserting glass tube through stopper.

PROCEDURE:

1. Make a filtration tower by inserting a glass tube into a one-hole stopper.
2. Insert rubber stopper into glass cylinder and fasten entire structure to a ring stand and clamp as illustrated.
3. Place beaker under glass tube.
4. First add sand (to 5 cm thickness) then fine gravel, and finally coarse gravel.
5. Pour 50 mL muddy water into filtration tower.

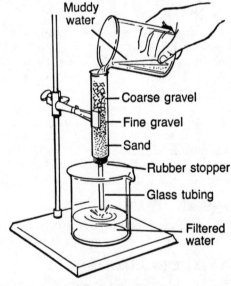

FIGURE 13-1

OBSERVATIONS AND DATA:

The muddy water clears is it passes through filtration tower.

QUESTIONS AND CONCLUSIONS:

The sand and gravel are filters that can be used to separate the mud from the water.

1. Are any bacteria that were present in the original water killed as it passes through the filtration tower?   *no*

2. How does well water become clear? *Groundwater is filtered as it passes through different layers of soil and dirt until it is relatively pure. Wells are dug deep enough to tap into these underground streams.*
3. Why would you want to add charcoal to this tower. *It removes objectionable odors.*

ADDITIONAL ACTIVITY: Differences between Hard and Soft Water (section 13:8)

OBJECTIVE: To produce suds with soap, using hard and soft water

CLASS TIME ALLOTMENT: 15 minutes.

MATERIALS:

hard water, 250 mL
liquid soap

Erlenmeyer flasks, 250 mL—2
washing soda (Na_2CO_3)

PREPARATION NOTES:

Prepare hard water by adding 25 g $CaCl_2$ to 250 mL distilled water. Liquid soap may be prepared by dissolving soap flakes, available from a local grocery store, in distilled water. Flasks are easier to use than test tubes in this activity. Ask students to read the contents of washing soda and have them relate this to test and the sodium zeolite used in water softeners. In this way they can understand the process of water softening better.

PROCEDURE:

1. Obtain or make 250 mL of hard water. Place 125 mL in each of two Erlenmeyer flasks.
2. Place several drops of liquid soap in each flask and shake. Observe results.
3. Dissolve one teaspoon of washing soda in one of the two flasks. Shake.
4. Observe, compare and explain the difference in the two test tubes.

OBSERVATIONS AND DATA:

The amount of soap suds in the flask with the washing soda is greater than in the other flask.

QUESTIONS AND CONCLUSIONS:

Washing soda removes the calcium from hard water, producing soft water. The soft water allows more suds to form.
1. What substance is added to water when water softeners containing zeolite are used? *sodium*
2. Which type of water is best to use when washing clothes? *soft water* Why? *Hard water produces calcium, magnesium, or iron precipitates, which then form on clothes.*

CHALLENGE: APPLYING SCIENTIFIC METHODS
Classification of Plastics

OBJECTIVE: To classify some common plastics

CLASS TIME ALLOTMENT: One period.

MATERIALS:

apron
beaker, 400 mL
burner
goggles
matches
plastic samples

ring stand and ring
tongs
towel
water
wire gauze
cloth towel

PREPARATION NOTES:

In this activity, students warm several different plastic items to determine if they are thermoplastics or thermosetting plastics. Thermoplastics can be remolded after they have set. Plastics that cannot be remolded after they have set are thermosetting plastics. Items you may wish to have students experiment with include a pen cap, plastic tablecloth, switch plate, toothbrush handle, plastic jewelry, baby bottle, plastic tubing, comb, and a record album. Caution students to wear goggles and aprons and to handle hot plastics with tongs or a towel.

PROCEDURE:

1. Assemble a wire gauze and ring stand.
2. Fill a 400 mL beaker about ¾ full of water. Place on wire gauze.
3. Heat the water until it boils. **CAUTION:** Wear apron and goggles.
4. With tongs, place each sample of plastic one piece at a time into the boiling water. Heat for 5 minutes.
5. At the end of 5 minutes, take the plastic out with the tongs. Set the plastic on the table and, using the cloth, try to bend the plastic while it is still warm. **CAUTION:** Plastic may be hot. If the plastic bends and changes shape, it is a thermoplastic. If not, it is a thermosetting plastic.
6. Repeat Steps 4 and 5 for each plastic sample. Record all results.

OBSERVATIONS AND DATA:

The pen cap and switch plate do not bend, and thus are thermosetting plastics. The other suggested samples bend when heated and thus are thermoplastics.

QUESTIONS AND CONCLUSIONS:

1. (a) Plastic combs are made of nylon. Would nylon be used to make television cabinets?   *No*
   (b) Explain.   *The cabinet would be subjected to heat. A cabinet made of nylon would deform.*
2. Polystyrene is used to make plastic bags. What property of polystyrene makes it ideal for plastic raincoats?   *Polystyrene has a high degree of flexibility.*
3. What type of plastic should be used for making dinnerware?   *Dinnerware should be made of a thermosetting plastic.*
4. Some plastics become brittle when they become cold.
   (a) Would this be an important factor if the plastic were used in an automobile?   *Yes*
   (b) Explain.   *The plastic would crack when subjected to the cold outdoor temperatures.*

UNIT FOUR

Energy

chapter 14

Heat

ACTIVITY 14-1: Heat and Metals (page 270)

OBJECTIVE: To observe how a change in temperature causes a metal to expand or contract

CLASS TIME ALLOTMENT: 15 minutes.

MATERIALS:

iron ball and ring	matches
bimetallic strip	clock or watch
burner	

PREPARATION NOTES:

In this activity, the student observes how a change in temperature causes a metal to expand or contract.

PROCEDURE:

1. Obtain an iron ball and ring and a bimetallic strip. (You may wish to do this as a demonstration.)
2. Try to pass the ball through the ring. Observe what happens.
3. Heat the ball in a flame for 30 seconds. Try to pass the ball through the ring again. Observe what happens.
4. Observe the bimetallic strip and record which side of the strip is toward the desk. Heat this side of the strip over a flame. Observe what happens.
5. Let the strip cool, and then heat the other side. Observe what happens.

OBSERVATIONS AND DATA:

At first, the ball passes through the ring. After it is heated, the ball does not pass through the ring. When the bimetallic strip is heated, it bends in one direction. When the other side is heated, it bends in the same direction as before.

QUESTIONS AND CONCLUSIONS:

The bimetallic strip bends in only one direction when heated.
1. What effect does heat have on the metal ball?   *The metal ball expands when heated.*
2. Why does the bimetallic strip bend?   *It bends because of the unequal expansion of the two strips of different metals that are welded together.*

ACTIVITY 14-2: Heat and Changes in State (page 272)

OBJECTIVE: To observe temperature change as ice changes to water and as water is boiled to steam, and to draw a graph to illustrate the observed change

CLASS TIME ALLOTMENT: 30 minutes.

MATERIALS:

beaker, 250 mL
ice
thermometer, Celsius
hot plate
clock or watch
graph paper

PREPARATION NOTES:

In this activity the student draws a graph to illustrate an observed temperature change as ice changes to water and as water is boiled to steam. Review procedures for constructing graphs before students begin work. Use the chalkboard to explain how to plot temperature changes over time. Time is plotted on the horizontal axis and °C on the vertical axis.

PROCEDURE:

1. Fill a beaker one-half full of ice. Record the temperature of the ice.
2. Gently heat the beaker of ice on a hot plate.
3. Record the temperature of the icewater every 2 min until the water boils.
4. Draw a graph of temperature versus time.

OBSERVATIONS AND DATA:

Student graphs should resemble this graph. (This graph is the same as Figure 14-4, page 271.) The shape should be similar.

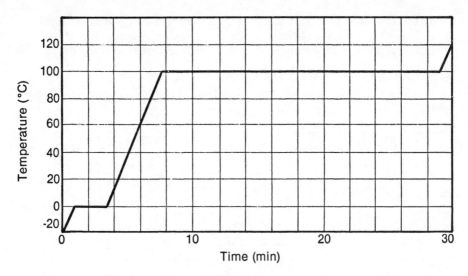

FIGURE 14-1

QUESTIONS AND CONCLUSIONS:

1. Why does the temperature rise at first and then remain constant? *Temperature is constant while ice is melting.*
2. What does the graph look like at 100°C when water boils? *Temperature increases as water is heated to 100°C; is constant as water boils.*
3. What process occurs at 0°C? at 100°C? *melting; boiling*
4. How does your graph compare with Figure 14-4? *the graphs should be similar in shape*

ACTIVITY 14-3: Specific Heat (page 274)

OBJECTIVE: To compare the rates of heating of sand and water, thereby illustrating the concept of specific heats of different substances

CLASS TIME ALLOTMENT: 25 minutes.

MATERIALS:

cans, small—2   sand
thermometer, Celsius—2   lamp
water   clock or watch

PREPARATION NOTES:

In this activity the student compares the rates of heating of sand and water, thereby illustrating the concept of specific heats of different substances.

PROCEDURE:

1. Obtain two empty soup cans.
2. Place a thermometer in each can.

3. Fill one can ⅔ full of water. Fill the second can ⅔ full of sand.
4. Place both cans in bright sunlight or under a lamp.
5. Record the temperature of each substance every 2 min for 15 min.

OBSERVATIONS AND DATA:

The temperature of the sand increased faster than the temperature of the water.

TIME	TEMPERATURE
2 min	
4 min	
6 min	
8 min	
10 min	
12 min	
14 min	

QUESTIONS AND CONCLUSIONS:

1. In which can did the temperature increase faster?   *sand*
2. Which substance, sand or water, has the higher specific heat?   *water*
   Sand has a lower specific heat than water. It gains and loses heat faster than water.

ADDITIONAL QUESTIONS:

3. Which gains and loses heat faster, water or sand? Why?   *sand; sand transfers heat faster than water because it has a lower specific heat*
4. How does the difference in the specific heat of sand and water affect the temperatures around oceans and lakes?   *Since water gains and loses heat more slowly than the sand, land areas surrounded by water are more moderate in temperature. The water prevents extremely high and low temperatures.*
5. How is the plant and animal population of an area affected by the presence of a large body of water?   *The extremes of temperature to which a given piece of land is subjected determine the kind of plants and animals that can grow in that area.*

ADDITIONAL ACTIVITY: Which Metal Melts the Most Paraffin? (section 14:5)

OBJECTIVE: To compare the amounts of heat released from different metals, each of equal mass and heated to the same temperature

CLASS TIME ALLOTMENT: 20 minutes.

MATERIALS:

beaker, 400 mL
Bunsen burner or other heat source
paraffin
pieces of 3 different metals,
  all the same mass
  (e.g., aluminum, copper, iron)

ring stand and ring
tongs
water, 300 mL

PREPARATION NOTES:

In this activity there is a direct relationship between the paraffin melted and the specific heat because the mass of the substance and the temperature change are the same for all three metals.

PROCEDURE:

1. Heat 300 mL of water to boiling in a 400 mL beaker.
2. Place the three pieces of metal in the beaker of boiling water. Heat for 5 minutes.
3. Using the tongs, remove each metal piece and place each on a separate paraffin block.
4. Observe which metal melts the most paraffin.

OBSERVATIONS AND DATA:

The paraffin wax melts under all three metals. Aluminum melts more wax than the other two metals. Iron melts more wax than copper.

QUESTIONS AND CONCLUSIONS:

Aluminum releases the largest amount of heat of the metals tested. Copper releases the smallest amount of heat.
1. Which metal loses the most heat?   *aluminum*
2. Which metal has highest specific heat? Lowest?   *aluminum; copper*
3. How does heat loss vary with specific heat (when mass and temperature change are held constant)?   *The larger the specific heat, the greater the heat loss.*
4. Why should the three pieces of metal have equal masses?   *so that the direct relationship between heat loss and specific heat can be observed*

ACTIVITY 14:4: Calorimeter (page 275)

OBJECTIVE: To construct a calorimeter and calculate the heat loss from a piece of aluminum heated to 100°C.

CLASS TIME ALLOTMENT: One period.

MATERIALS:

can, large
can, small
vermiculite, 1 bag
cardboard
scissors
stirring rod, wood
thermometer
water
beaker, 250 mL
hot plate
aluminum sample
tongs
clock or watch

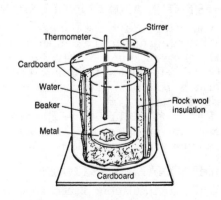

FIGURE 14-2

PREPARATION NOTES:

In this activity the student constructs a calorimeter to calculate the heat loss from a piece of heated aluminum. Demonstrate the assembly of the calorimeter and the procedure for this activity before students begin work. Discuss the function of each part of the calorimeter. Remind students to use tongs in handling the hot piece of aluminum. It may be helpful to measure the amount of vermiculite needed to fill the space between the two cans and have this amount prepackaged in small bags.

PROCEDURE:

1. Obtain a small and large can. Fill the bottom of the larger can with vermiculite.
2. Place the smaller can inside the larger one and fill the space between the cans with more vermiculite.
3. Cut a cardboard cover for the cans. Make two small holes in the center of the cardboard cover.
4. Insert a wooden rod through one hole and a thermometer through the other hole.
5. Add 200 mL water to the inner can and record its temperature.
6. Heat a thick piece of aluminum in boiling water for 5 minutes.
7. Add the aluminum to the water in the calorimeter. Replace the lid.
8. Stir the water and record the temperature every two minutes for 10 minutes.

OBSERVATIONS AND DATA:

The temperature of the water increased, and the temperature of the aluminum decreased.

TEMPERATURE DATA CHART

WATER	ALUMINUM	ALUMINUM IN WATER
		2 min
		4 min
		6 min
		8 min
		10 min

QUESTIONS AND CONCLUSIONS:

1. What happened to the temperature of the water?   *increased*
2. What happened to the temperature of the metal?   *decreased*
3. How do you know?   *the water gained heat*
4. Calculate the joules of heat absorbed by the water. Calculation of joules of heat is based on the change in temperature of the water in the calorimeter.
   $H = \Delta t \times 4.18J/g \cdot C° \times 200$ g) *200 mL of water equals 200 g($t_2 - t_1$)*
5. How do you determine the number of joules of heat released by the aluminum?   *It is the same as the number of joules absorbed by the water.*

ADDITIONAL QUESTIONS:

6. Why was insulation placed around bottom and sides of the small can?   *to prevent heat loss to the surroundings*

ACTIVITY 14-5: Heat Transfer (page 278)

OBJECTIVE: To investigate the transfer of heat by conduction and radiation

CLASS TIME ALLOTMENT: 30 minutes.

MATERIALS:

knitting needle, metal
cork
ring stand/clamp
candle
matches
clock or watch
glycerol

glass rod, 15 cm
towel, cloth
light source
prism
stopper, 1-hole—2
thermometer

PREPARATION NOTES:

In this activity the student investigates the transfer of heat by conduction and radiation. Review the customary cautions in working with hot objects and open flames. Remind students to hold the knitting needle and glass rod over a piece of paper when dripping wax onto the needle and the rod. Demonstrate the use of a prism to produce a spectrum by shining a beam of light at the prism and projecting the spectrum onto a piece of cardboard.

PROCEDURE:

1. Push one end of a metal knitting needle into a cork. Clamp the cork to a ring stand.
2. Light a candle and turn it to the side to allow 4 small pieces of wax to drip about 3 cm apart on the knitting needle.
3. Place the lighted candle under the pointed end of the knitting needle. **CAUTION:** Be sure to keep your hair and clothes away from the flame.
4. Record the time it takes for all the wax to drip off the needle.
5. Place a drop of glycerol on the tip of a glass rod 15 cm long. Using a towel to hold the rod, carefully insert it into a 1-hole stopper. Clamp the stopper to a ring stand.
6. Place 4 pieces of wax about 3 cm apart on the glass rod.
7. Use the lighted candle to heat the glass rod for the same length of time you heated the needle. Record your observations.
8. Using a light source, produce a rainbow with a prism.
9. Using the procedure described in Step 5, insert the top of a thermometer in a 1-hole stopper and clamp it to a ring stand.
10. Position the thermometer to the right of the red band of color. Record the temperature. Wait 5 minutes. Record the temperature again.

OBSERVATIONS AND DATA:

The wax on the glass rod melted all at once, and more slowly than the wax on the metal rod. Wax on the metal knitting needle did not melt all at once. The thermometer near the red end of the spectrum showed an increase in temperature.

QUESTIONS AND CONCLUSIONS:

1. Which method of heat transfer is demonstrated by heating the knitting needle? *conduction*

2. What happened to the wax when you heated the glass rod? Explain. *The wax on the glass rod did not melt as quickly as the wax on the needle because glass is not as good a conductor as metal.*
3. Explain any changes in recorded temperature of thermometer placed near red band of spectrum. *Infrared radiation caused the temperature to rise.*
4. What type of heat transfer does this procedure illustrate? *radiation*

ADDITIONAL QUESTIONS:

5. Why did the wax nearest the flame on the knitting needle melt first? *Metal is a better conductor of heat than glass.*
6. Why did the wax pieces on the glass rod melt at approximately the same time? *Heat is more readily conducted through the glass.*
7. Why is heat conducted better in metals than glass? *Metals conduct heat better because their atoms are packed more closely together. Thus, it takes less time for heat to pass from one atom to the next atom.*

ACTIVITY 14-6: Insulation (page 280)

OBJECTIVE: To investigate the effectiveness of selected insulators

CLASS TIME ALLOTMENT: One period.

MATERIALS:

can, small—4	aluminum foil
can, large	hot plate
vermiculite, 1 bag	tea kettle
water	protective gloves
graduated cylinder, 25 mL	thermometer—4
marking pencil	graph paper
	clock or watch

PREPARATION NOTES:

In this activity the student investigates the effectiveness of selected insulators. Explain the procedure used in marking the containers to the 400-mL level. Remind students to follow normal cautionary procedures when handling hot water and thermometers. Use the chalkboard to show how data is recorded. When graphing, plot minutes on the X-axis and temperature on the Y-axis.

PROCEDURE:

1. Obtain 4 small cans, 1 large can, and a bag of vermiculite.
2. Using tap water and a graduated cylinder, add 400 mL water to one can. Mark the 400-mL level. Use this water to determine and mark the 400-mL level in each can. Then pour the water into a sink.
3. Cover one small can with aluminum foil, shiny side toward the can.
4. Cover another small can with aluminum foil, shiny side out.
5. Leave the third small can uncovered.
6. Set up the last small can and the large can like a calorimeter (page 275).

7. Heat 2 L water to 100°C in a tea kettle on a hot plate. Use protective gloves to handle the tea kettle. Pour hot water into each container to the 400 mL mark. Put a thermometer into each container and record the temperature every 2 minutes for 20 minutes. Draw a graph of temperature versus time for each container.

OBSERVATIONS AND DATA:

	TIME (minutes)									
	2	4	6	8	10	12	14	16	18	20
can with shiny side out										
can with shiny side in										
uncovered can										
can set up like calorimeter										

The temperature drops (most slowly) in the can surrounded by vermiculite; the uncovered can cools fastest. Can with shiny side of foil facing inward cools more slowly than can with shiny side of soil facing out. Have students use different colors of ink to represent each container on their graph.

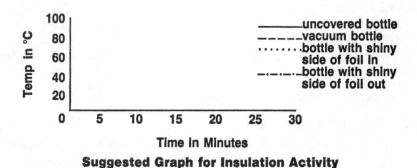

Suggested Graph for Insulation Activity

FIGURE 14-3

QUESTIONS AND CONCLUSIONS:

Vermiculite-insulated and foil-covered containers with the shiny side of foil facing inward are the best containers for preventing heat loss.
1. In which container did the water cool fastest?   *uncovered can* Slowest?   *can surrounded with vermiculite*
2. How was heat transferred from the containers?   *conduction; radiation*
3. Which container had the best insulation for this type of heat transfer?   *can surrounded with vermiculite*
4. Why was one can left uncovered?   *control for comparison*

ADDITIONAL QUESTIONS:

5. Why does the can that has the shiny side of the aluminum foil facing in lose heat more slowly?   *The shiny surface reflects heat from the can.*
6. How could you wrap foods that are hot to keep them warm?   *wrap with aluminum foil so that the shiny side is next to the food*

7. How does the vacuum between walls of a vacuum bottle prevent heat loss? *The partial vacuum between walls of the vacuum bottle prevents loss of heat by conduction because there are few molecules of air to conduct the heat.*
8. Why would a vacuum bottle be a good container for preventing heat loss? *A vacuum bottle prevents heat loss in two ways: (1) the shiny surface reduces heat loss by radiation and (2) the partial vacuum reduces heat transfer by conduction. NOTE: The scientific principles used in the vacuum bottle will be difficult to understand since students need firsthand experience with vacuums to appreciate the construction. However, the use of the silvered surfaces in a vacuum bottle may be appreciated because they can relate this to the glass bottle with the aluminum foil whose shiny side faces inward.*

ADDITIONAL ACTIVITY: Heating Water with Steam (section 14:9)

OBJECTIVE: To see the heating effect of steam in contact with tap water

CLASS TIME ALLOTMENT: One period.

MATERIALS:

beaker, 250 mL	glycerol
burner or other heat source	towel
glass delivery tube, 45 cm	test tube, 20 x 200 mm
goggles	test tube clamp
ring stand	thermometer, Celsius
rubber stopper, 1 hole, to fit test tube	water

PREPARATION NOTES:

In this activity, students investigate the effect of steam when it comes into contact with room temperature water. It is recommended that this activity be performed as a demonstration. Steam is extremely hot and can cause severe burns. Be extremely careful that the stopper does not pop off the end of the test tube due to the pressure of the steam.

PROCEDURE:

1. Fill large test tube ⅓ full of water.
2. Insert glass delivery tube into rubber stopper. **CAUTION:** Moisten end of glass tube with glycerol. Hold the glass with a rag or towel as you insert it into stopper.
3. Place stopper in test tube.
4. Attach test tube to ring stand with clamp. Test tube should be in a slanted position, as shown in diagram.
5. Place end of delivery tube in 250 mL beaker that contains 100 mL of water.
6. Record temperature of water in beaker.
7. Heat water in test tube until steam comes through delivery tube. **CAUTION:** Steam causes very severe burns. Allow steam to bubble through water for 5 minutes. Record temperature.
8. Remove delivery tube from beaker. Remove heat from test tube. Record temperature.

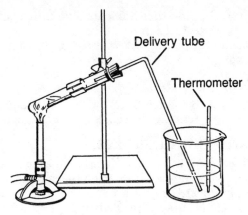

Delivery tube

Thermometer

FIGURE 14-4

OBSERVATIONS AND DATA:

The temperature of the water increases when steam is bubbled through it, then decreases when steam is removed.

QUESTIONS AND CONCLUSIONS:

Heat can be transferred when a gas is in contact with a liquid. As steam cools, the water gains heat.
1. How does the amount of heat in the water change? *increases*
2. How? *It increases as the steam cools.*
3. What change in your equipment would be needed if you wanted to measure the heat gained by the water? *The water in the beaker would have to be insulated so heat would not escape.*

ADDITIONAL ACTIVITY: Cooling Effect of Evaporation (section 14:10)

OBJECTIVE: To observe the temperature drop that occurs when water evaporates.

CLASS TIME ALLOTMENT: 15 minutes.

MATERIALS:

beaker or pan to hold water
cotton cloth, small piece
electric fan or hand fan

thermometer, Celsius
water

PREPARATION NOTES:

In this activity, students investigate the temperature change that occurs as water evaporates. Meteorologists use a technique similar to this in determining dew point temperature and saturation point for air humidity.

PROCEDURE:

1. Wrap bulb of thermometer with dry cotton cloth. Record temperature.
2. Hold thermometer in path of fan or wind. Record any temperature change that occurs.

3. Moisten cotton by dipping thermometer bulb into a beaker of water at room temperature. Record temperature.
4. Hold thermometer in same wind source as in Step 2. Record any temperature change.

OBSERVATIONS AND DATA:

When cotton cloth is dry, temperature does not change. When cloth is damp, the temperature reading decreases as thermometer is fanned.

QUESTIONS AND CONCLUSIONS:

Evaporation of water removes heat from a substance that is wet.
1. What happened to the temperature when thermometer was wrapped in wet cloth and placed in front of a fan?   *The temperature decreased.*
2. What phase change occurs in this activity?   *evaporation; liquid to gas*
3. Is heat needed to change a liquid to a gas? Where does this heat come from?   *yes; the surroundings*
4. Why does the temperature reading decrease when the water evaporates?   *Heat is taken from the cloth and thermometer and added to the water.*

CHALLENGE: APPLYING SCIENTIFIC METHODS
Heat and Temperature Change

OBJECTIVE: To determine the amount of heat needed to cause a temperature change in water

CLASS TIME ALLOTMENT: One period.

MATERIALS:

apron	glycerin, 130 mL	thermometer, Celcius
beakers, 250 mL, 2	goggles	towel
beam balance	matches	watch or clock
burner	ring stand and ring	water, 100 mL
buret clamp	rubber stopper, 1-hole	wire gauze

PREPARATION NOTES:

In this activity students determine the temperature change that occurs when two liquids are heated to 75°C, and then calculate the number of joules used in this temperature change. Students also compare the time it takes to heat each liquid with its specific heat. Caution students to wear goggles and aprons when heating liquids. When assembling apparatus, students should moisten the thermometer with water or glycerin before inserting it into the stopper. Students should also wrap their hands in cloth towels before gently twisting the thermometer into the stopper. Students should also be advised not to allow the thermometer to come into contact with the beaker during the heating process.

PROCEDURE:

1. Find the mass of an empty 250-mL beaker on a beam balance and record.
2. Set the beam balance to read 100 g more than the mass of the beaker. Pour water into the beaker until the balance just tips.

3. Measure the exact mass of the water and beaker.
4. Place the beaker on a wire gauze that is set on a ring stand.
5. Place the thermometer in the rubber stopper. **CAUTION:** Moisten the end of the thermometer with mineral oil or glycerin. Hold the thermometer with a towel as you slide it into the stopper.
6. Fasten the rubber stopper to the ring stand so that the bulb of the thermometer is in the water. Record the temperature. **CAUTION:** Position the thermometer so that it does not touch the bottom or sides of the beaker.
7. Begin heating the water over a low flame. Record the time you begin heating.
8. Heat the water gently until the temperature reaches 75°C. Remove the heat. Record the time heating ceased.
9. After removing the heat, continue to read the thermometer until the temperature reaches its highest point. Record this peak temperature.
10. Repeat steps 1 through 9 using glycerin instead of water. Be sure that the flame height of the burner is the same as you used for the water.
11. Calculate the mass of each liquid by subtracting the mass of the beaker from the combined mass of the beaker and liquid. Record these masses.
12. Calculate the temperature change for each liquid by subtracting the beginning temperature (Step 6) from the peak temperature (Step 9).
13. Calculate the time used to heat each liquid to 75°C.
14. Calculate the amount of heat that each liquid gained by using the following equation.

Heat = Mass × specific heat × temperature change
Specific heat of water = 4.18 J/g·C°
Specific heat of glycerin = 2.51 J/g·C°

OBSERVATIONS AND DATA:

Student data will vary, but should be similar to that listed here. If the mass of the water is 101.4 g and it took 3 minutes to produce a 60°C temperature change, the heat gained is 25 400 J. If the mass of glycerin is 100.6 g and it took 2 minutes to produce a 59°C temperature change, the heat gained is 14 800 J.

QUESTIONS AND CONCLUSIONS:

1. If 150 g of glycerin were heated from 35°C to 93°C, how many joules of heat would be needed?   *Heat gained = 150g × 2.51 J/g·C° × (93°C − 35°C) = 21 800 J*
2. (a) Is there a difference between temperature change and heat?   *yes*
   (b) In what unit is temperature change measured?   *Celsius degrees (°C)*
   (c) In what unit is heat measured?   *joules (J)*
3. What other quantities must be used to calculate heat besides temperature change?   *The mass of the material and its specific heat must be used.*
4. (a) Does the number of joules needed to heat a substance depend on the nature of the substance?   *yes*
   (b) What quality tells you this?   *The heat gained depends upon the specific heat of the substance.*
5. (a) Which liquid needed more time to reach 75°C?   *water*
   (b) Does this liquid have the higher or lower specific heat?   *higher*

6. (a) A substance has a specific heat of 4.0 J/g·C°. Would it take more, less, or the same amount of time to heat 100 g of this substance to 75°C than it would water using the same heat source? *It would take less time than 100 g of water.*
   (b) Would it require more or less heat? *It would require less heat than 100 g of water.*
7. Why does the temperature continue to rise after the heat source is removed? *The glass beaker absorbs heat from the burner. Some of this heat is transferred to the water after the heat source is removed.*

---

chapter 15

Sound and Light

ADDITIONAL ACTIVITY: Waves in a Rope (section 15:2)

OBJECTIVE: To examine the direction in which transverse waves travel

CLASS TIME ALLOTMENT: 10 minutes.

MATERIALS:
door with doorknob
rope, 4.5 m

PREPARATION NOTES:
   Be sure to use a good heavy rope. This activity would make a good homework assignment.

PROCEDURE:
1. Tie one end of a rope to a doorknob.
2. Shake the loose end so waves are produced in the rope.
3. Make a diagram of the waves. Draw arrows to show the direction in which the rope vibrates and the direction in which the wave travels.

OBSERVATIONS AND DATA:

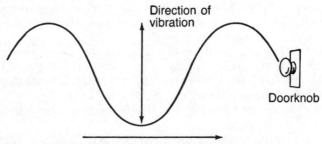

FIGURE 15-1 Direction in which wave travels

QUESTIONS AND CONCLUSIONS:

1. Name some examples of tranverse waves. *light waves, water waves, waves in a rope*
2. What is the wavelength of a transverse wave? *The wavelength is the distance from one high point in the rope to the next high point.*
3. How does a transverse wave travel? *Transverse waves travel away from the source or origin. In a transverse wave, vibrations are at right angles to the direction of the wave.*

ACTIVITY 15-1: Reflection and Refraction (page 299)

OBJECTIVE: To investigate the concept of refraction and reflection using a rubber ball and two small wheels mounted on an axle

CLASS TIME ALLOTMENT: 30 minutes.

MATERIALS: ball, rubber   cloth, soft   toy wheels with axle
chalk   protractor

PREPARATION NOTES:

In this activity the student investigates the concept of refraction and reflection using a rubber ball and two small wheels mounted on an axle. As a reference for measuring the angles of incidence and reflection, draw a chalk line perpendicular to the wall. Have students roll the ball at an angle to the point of intersection and compare the angles on each side of the line produced by the path of the rolling ball. Toy wheels and axles may be obtained from old discarded toys.

PROCEDURE:

1. Roll a ball so that it strikes a wall at a 90° angle. Record the angle of reflection.
2. Roll a ball toward the wall at another angle.
3. Repeat Step 2 by rolling the ball toward the wall at several different angles. Mark the path of the ball with chalk. Measure and compare the angle of incidence and the angle of reflection.
4. Mount 2 toy wheels on an axle. Roll the axle at an angle toward a soft cloth which is on a smooth surface. Record your observations.

OBSERVATIONS AND DATA:

Wall

FIGURE 15-2

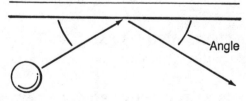
Angle

The ball in Step 1 is reflected at a 90° angle. In Steps 2 and 3, the angle of incidence and the angle of reflection are equal. In Step 4, the wheel that hits the cloth first slows down. The other wheel and the axle turn toward the cloth.

QUESTIONS AND CONCLUSIONS:

1. When the ball is rolled toward the wall at several different angles, how do the angles of incidence and reflection compare?   *They are equal.*
2. What happens to the wheel of the wheel and axle that hits the cloth first?   *It slows down.*
3. What happens to the speed and direction of the other wheel and the axle?   *They turn toward the cloth.*
4. How is this example similar to refraction?   *The turn in the path of the wheels is similar to the bending of a wave in refraction.*

ADDITIONAL QUESTIONS:

5. How is the reflection of a light ray similar to reflection of a rubber ball?   *The angle at which a light ray is reflected is equal to the angle at which it strikes a surface.*
6. How could this activity help a basketball player in shooting baskets?   *When using the backboard for a shot, the ball will bounce off the boards at the same angle as it is thrown against the boards. A player can practice throwing the ball off the boards at the proper angle.*
7. How are the laws of reflection important in the game of ice hockey?   *The goalie can control the direction of the puck's rebound by pointing the hockey stick in the proper direction; passes are sometimes made by bouncing the puck off the wall.*

ADDITIONAL ACTIVITY: Using a Light Meter (section 15:6)

OBJECTIVE: To use a light meter to measure illumination

CLASS TIME ALLOTMENT: 15 minutes.

MATERIALS:

light meter   light sources

PREPARATION NOTES:

This activity may be done at home if sufficient light meters are available.

PROCEDURE:

1. Use the light meter to record the light outside on a sunny day.
2. Use the light meter to measure the illumination of various places in your home or school.

OBSERVATIONS AND DATA:

The brighter the light shining on a given area, the higher the meter reading will be.

QUESTIONS AND CONCLUSIONS:

A light meter can be used to measure illumination. Illumination varies with the light source and with distance from the source.

1. What does a light meter measure?   *illumination*

2. How does a light meter work? *Light hitting a photocell produces an electric current. This registers on the meter.*
3. Why do photographers use light meters? *to make sure the proper amount of light reaches the film. If a light meter shows that there is not enough light, the photographer can open up the shutter to allow more light to reach the film.*

ADDITIONAL ACTIVITY: Optical Illusions (section 15:7)

OBJECTIVE: To discover that the dimensions of objects can look different than they really are

CLASS TIME ALLOTMENT: 15 minutes.

MATERIALS:
metric ruler

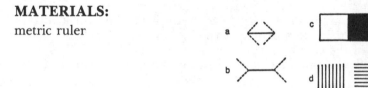

FIGURE 15-3

PROCEDURE:
1. Look at lines a and b in Figure 15-3. Predict which line is longer without measuring the lines.
2. Now measure the lines.
3. Look at the black and white areas in c. Predict which area is larger.
4. Now measure them.
5. Look at the groups of lines in d. Predict which group has the widest lines.
6. Measure the widths of the lines.

OBSERVATIONS AND DATA:
Line b appears longer than a, but both are equal in length when measured. The white box appears larger than the black box, but both boxes are equal in area when measured. Vertical lines appear wider, but they are equal in width to the horizontal lines.

QUESTIONS AND CONCLUSIONS:
Dimensions of objects can appear to be different than they actually are.
1. Why do clothes designers use vertical lines more than horizontal lines? *Vertical lines make a person appear taller, slimmer; horizontal lines make a person appear shorter, heavier.*

ACTIVITY 15-2: Locating a Virtual Image (page 304)

OBJECTIVE: To form a virtual image and locate its position

CLASS TIME ALLOTMENT: 20 minutes.

MATERIALS:
mirror, plane
clay
candles, identical—2
candleholders—2
matches
ruler

PREPARATION NOTES:

In this activity, the student investigates the nature of a virtual image produced by a plane mirror. Be sure that both candles and candleholders are identical. Candles must be slightly taller than the mirror in order for an apparent lighted image to appear. Caution students to secure hair and loose clothing before lighting the candle.

PROCEDURE:

1. Make a mirror stand with the clay. Place the mirror and mirror stand on a table. Be sure that the mirror is perpendicular to the table.
2. Place each of the candles securely into a candleholder.
3. Using the ruler, position the center of one of the candles 5 cm in front of the mirror.
4. Place the second candle behind the mirror. Light the second candle. **CAUTION:** Secure hair and loose clothing before lighting the candle.
5. Watch the image of the unlit candle in the mirror. Have your partner carefully move the lighted candle behind the mirror until you observe that the image of the front candle appears to be lighted also. The candle image should appear to remain lighted from any viewing position.
6. Measure the distance from the reflecting surface of the mirror to the center of the lighted candle. Record your observations in a table similar to the one shown in Data and Observations.
7. Repeat Steps 2 through 6 with the center of the unlit candle at 10 cm and 20 cm from the reflecting surface of the mirror. Extinguish the candle as soon as you finish the procedure.

OBSERVATIONS AND DATA:

DISTANCE FROM MIRROR	
Unlighted candle	Lighted candle
5 cm	
10 cm	
20 cm	

QUESTIONS AND CONCLUSIONS:

1. What type of image was formed by the mirror? Write a definition of this type of image based on your observations. *A virtual image was formed. A virtual image is formed without light rays passing through it.*
2. Where was the candle image located? How do you know? *The image was located as far behind the mirror as the candle was in front of the mirror. When the lighted image appeared, the lighted image was the same distance behind the mirror as the unlighted candle was in front of the mirror.*
3. If you placed a piece of paper where the candle image appeared to be, what would you observe? *No image would appear on the paper.*

4. A candle is placed 1 m in front of the reflecting surface of a plane mirror. How far from the reflecting surface will the image appear to be? Explain. *The image will appear 1 m behind the mirror. See question 2 for explanation.*
5. In a small room, why might a decorator use mirrors to panel one wall? *The mirrors make the room appear to be twice as large.*

ADDITIONAL ACTIVITY: Refraction in Water (section 15:8)

OBJECTIVE: To see an effect of refraction

CLASS TIME ALLOTMENT: 15 minutes.

MATERIALS: drinking glass, round, clear glass
ruler
water

PREPARATION NOTES:

In this activity, students observe the effects of refraction. Refraction is the bending of light as it passes from one medium to another. In this activity, light rays are bent as they pass from water to air. Refraction makes objects that are immersed in both media appear to be bent or divided into two pieces.

PROCEDURE:

1. Place ruler in a round drinking glass that is two-thirds full of water. Rest ruler at angle against the side of the glass.
2. Observe ruler at the water line. You should make sure your eye is level with water line. NOTE: Try to get students to focus eyes on the boundary line where water and air meet.

OBSERVATIONS AND DATA:

The ruler appears to bend at the water line and top part of the ruler appears to be horizontally displaced from the bottom part of the ruler.

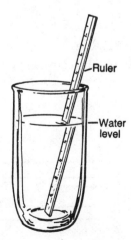

FIGURE 15-4

QUESTIONS AND CONCLUSIONS:

Light rays are bent as they pass from water to air. This makes objects that are immersed in both mediums appear to be bent or divided into two pieces.

1. Why does the ruler appear to be bent or divided when part of it is in water?   *Light waves from bottom part of ruler change direction as they pass from water into air. Light waves from top part of ruler do not change direction. Because only the bottom waves change direction, the ruler appears bent or divided.*
2. What is the name that is used to refer to the bending of light waves?   *refraction*
3. Does the speed of light change as light passes from water into air? How?   *yes; It decreases.*

ACTIVITY 15-3: Refraction of Light (page 305)

OBJECTIVE: To observe the refraction of light

CLASS TIME ALLOTMENT: 30 minutes.

MATERIALS:

coin
baking dish, shallow
water

PREPARATION NOTES:

In this activity the student observes the refraction of light that occurs when the light passes through water. A critical factor in this activity is that the observer moves forward towards the pan to the point where the coin just disappears from view. The observer must then stand perfectly straight and not move as the water is poured into the pan.

PROCEDURE:

1. Place a coin in the bottom of a shallow baking pan.
2. Have your laboratory partner stand away from pan at the place where the sides of the pan just block the view of the coin. Your partner should be able to see part of the bottom of the pan.
3. Fill pan with water.
4. Ask partner if the coin can be seen.

OBSERVATIONS AND DATA:

Students should observe that the coin can be seen when water is added to the pan.

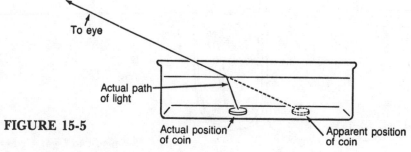

FIGURE 15-5

QUESTIONS AND CONCLUSIONS:

1. What does your partner observe?   *The coin is visible after water is added.*
2. How is this observation an example of refraction?   *The light waves entering air from the water are refracted, making the coin visible.*

ADDITIONAL QUESTIONS:

Light bending as it passes from water to air makes objects appear to change position.

3. Why can the coin be seen when the water is added?   *Light rays from the coin are refracted toward the horizontal as they leave the water. Thus, the coin appears to be farther from the observer than it really is.*
4. If you need to retrieve an object which has fallen into a swimming pool, would you dive in front of the object or behind the object?   *in front* Explain.   *Light coming from the object is refracted toward the horizontal as it leaves water. This makes the object appear to be farther from you than it actually is.*

ADDITIONAL ACTIVITY: Light into Color (section 15:9)

OBJECTIVE: To use a prism to produce a spectrum

CLASS TIME ALLOTMENT: 20 minutes.

MATERIALS:

cardboard, white—2 pieces
flashlight
fluorescent material, such as fluorite
prism

PREPARATION NOTES:

Students will have to spend time positioning prism to generate rainbow of color.

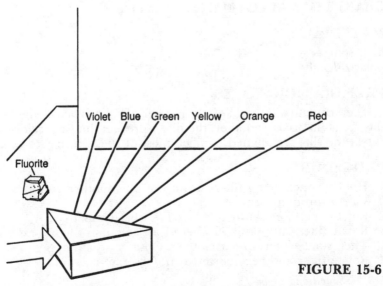

FIGURE 15-6

PROCEDURE:

1. Cut out a disc of cardboard that is just large enough to cover lens of flashlight.
2. Cut a small circle, about 0.5 cm diameter, in the center of the cardboard disc. Tape disc to lens of flashlight.
3. Place triangular prism on a table or book and set up a second piece of white cardboard as shown in the above Figure.
4. Darken room and turn on flashlight.
5. Observe and record what you see on the white cardboard.
6. Place a fluorescent substance, such as the mineral fluorite, in space beyond violet part of spectrum. Record observations.

OBSERVATIONS AND DATA:

A rainbow of colors is projected on white cardboard placed in back of prism. Red is at the right, then orange, yellow, green, blue, and violet. A fluorite rock placed in region to left of violet band shows fluorescent glow.

QUESTIONS AND CONCLUSIONS:

Light can be broken up into its parts (spectra) when passed through a prism. Some of these parts, the parts beyond the red and violet bands, cannot be seen. The section beyond violet causes fluorescence.

1. Why does a rainbow occur when light is passed through a prism? *White light is broken up into its basic colors because different colors are refracted different amounts as they pass from air through glass and back to air.*
2. What happens to a fluorite rock placed in the region beyond violet light? Why? *The fluorite glows slightly. It glows because it contains matter that absorbs ultraviolet light and gives off visible light. The region beyond the violet is called the ultraviolet region.*

ADDITIONAL ACTIVITY: Polarized Light (section 15:10)

OBJECTIVE: To see the effect of filters on the passage of light

CLASS TIME ALLOTMENT: 15 minutes.

MATERIALS:

light source
polarizing filters

PREPARATION NOTES:

Filters contain slits that allow the passage of light. When aligned so that the slits are at 90° to one another, the filters prevent the passage of most light. When the slits are aligned parallel, most of the light passes through.

PROCEDURE:

1. Hold two polarizing filters on top of one another and look at a light source through them.
2. Rotate one filter slowly and observe what happens.
3. Rotate filters into position where least amount of light passes through. Then rotate filter a quarter turn. Observe what happens.
4. Rotate filter another quarter turn. Observe.

OBSERVATIONS AND DATA:

Depending on how the filters are aligned, a small amount or a large amount of light will pass through the filters. When you turn the filter a quarter turn, the amount of light changes from dark to light or light to dark.

QUESTIONS AND CONCLUSIONS:

When polarizing filters are arranged so that their slits are at 90° to one another, the filters prevent the passage of most of the light.
1. When do you see the brightest pattern of light? *when the filters are aligned so that their slits are parallel*
2. Why do you see no light when the slits are at 90° to one another? *When the filters are arranged so that their slits are at 90°, one filter prevents light from being passed in the up and down direction; the other in the sideways direction.*

CHALLENGE: APPLYING SCIENTIFIC METHODS
Separating White Light by Refraction

OBJECTIVE: To use a half prism to observe refraction

CLASS TIME ALLOTMENT: One period.

MATERIALS:

construction paper, black half prism (prism with a trapezoidal base)
file card, small, 2 scissors
flashlight tape

PREPARATION NOTES:

In this activity, students observe the path of light that has passed through different sides of a trapezoidal prism. A prism is a piece of transparent material that refracts light. When a beam of white light passes through a prism, the light is refracted. Refraction causes the beam of light to bend and separate into the colors of the visible spectrum. The lights in your classroom may need to be dimmed in order for students to see the path of light.

PROCEDURE:

1. Cut a piece of black construction paper to fit a small file card. Tape the construction paper on the file card.
2. Cut a slit 1 mm wide and 3.5 cm long in the file card. See Figure 15-7.
3. With tape, fasten the small and large cards together as shown in Figure 15-7. Make sure there is no tape along the slit.
4. Place the prism on the surface of the large file card. With the flashlight on the opposite side of the small card, shine a light through the slit. Rotate the prism so that the light hits one of the parallel sides of the prism at an angle. Record what happens to the light as it passes through the prism. Draw a diagram that shows the path of the light wave.
5. Change the angle at which the light beam hits the prism by rotating the prism. Observe the path of the light wave and draw a diagram.
6. Rotate and move the prism until you find a position in which the light wave is separated into its different colors. Draw a diagram of the light wave and prism.

OBSERVATIONS AND DATA:

Student diagrams should appear similar to those below. Diagrams show a top view of the prism.

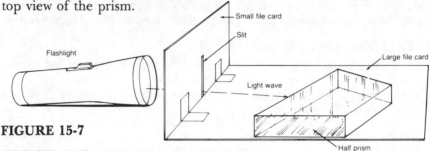

FIGURE 15-7

QUESTIONS AND CONCLUSIONS:

1. (a) How many times was the light wave bent or refracted as it passed through the prism?   *The light wave was refracted twice.*
   (b) Explain.   *The light wave is refracted as it enters the prism and is refracted as it leaves the prism.*
2. Explain what would happen if a light ray struck the prism at a 90° angle to the surface.   *The light ray would not be bent.*
3. Where must the light ray hit the prism in order for the light ray to break into colors?   *The light ray must enter the side of the prism near the corner with the acute angle. (See diagram for Step 6)*
4. What colors do you observe in the visible spectrum?   *The colors observed are violet, blue, green, yellow, orange, and red.*

---

chapter 16

Magnetism and Electricity

ACTIVITY 16-1: Magnets and Magnetic Fields (page 316)

OBJECTIVE: To observe the magnetic lines of force around a bar magnet and investigate the properties of attraction and repulsion of magnetic poles

CLASS TIME ALLOTMENT: 20 minutes.

MATERIALS:

bar magnet—2   paper, white
iron filings   string

PREPARATION NOTES:

In this activity the student observes the magnetic lines of force around a bar magnet and investigates the properties of attraction and repulsion of magnetic poles.

PROCEDURE:

1. Tie a thin string around the center of a magnet, and hang it from support.
2. Tie a second piece of string around the center of a second magnet.
3. Hold the string so the magnet swings freely. Be sure there is no metal in the area. Observe the direction in which the magnets point.
4. Bring the two north poles of the magnets close together. Observe what happens.
5. Bring both south poles together. Observe what happens.
6. Bring one north pole close to one south pole. Observe what happens.
7. Place one magnet under a piece of white paper. Sprinkle iron filings on the paper above the magnet. Tap the paper lightly. Observe the pattern formed.
8. Place both bar magnets under the paper with their north poles close together. Sprinkle iron filings on the paper. Observe the result.
9. Repeat Step 8 with one north pole facing one south pole. Observe the result.

OBSERVATIONS AND DATA:

When the magnets swing freely, they point toward each other. When the two north poles of the magnets are brought close together, they repel each other. The same thing happens when the two south poles are brought together. When one north pole is brought close to one south pole, they attract each other.

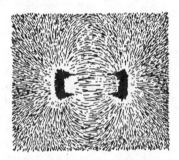

FIGURE 16-1

When a magnet is placed under the paper and iron filings are sprinkled on the paper, they form a pattern showing the magnetic field. When two magnets are placed under the paper with the north poles close to each other, and iron filings are sprinkled, few filings are between the poles. However, when the north and south poles face each other, there are iron filings between the poles.

QUESTIONS AND CONCLUSIONS:

1. In which direction do the magnets point when allowed to swing freely?   *towards each other*
2. What happens when two north or two south poles of the magnets are brought close together? Why?   *they repel each other; like poles repel each other*
3. Describe what happens when a north pole is brought close to a south pole.   *They attract each other.*

4. What kind of pattern is formed when iron filings are sprinkled on paper with a bar magnet under it? *The iron filings form a pattern showing the magnetic field.*
5. What kind of pattern is formed when two bar magnets are placed under a piece of paper with their north poles close together and filings are sprinkled on? *Very few filings are between the poles, showing that like poles repel.*
6. What kind of pattern is formed when two bar magnets with north and south poles close together are placed under paper and sprinkled with filings? *Iron filings form lines between the poles, showing that opposite poles attract.*

ACTIVITY 16-2: Electromagnets (page 319)

OBJECTIVE: To construct an electromagnet and observe its magnetic effect on various ferromagnetic substances

CLASS TIME ALLOTMENT: 30 minutes.

MATERIALS:
battery, 1½ v
bell wire, 20 cm
electric bell/switch
iron nail
paper clips—10
pins—10
tacks—10

PREPARATION NOTES:

In this activity the student constructs an electromagnet and observes its magnetic effect on various ferromagnetic substances. The action of an electromagnet in a bell is also observed. Students can measure the magnetic force of the electromagnet by observing the number of paper clips the electromagnet can pick up and hold in a chain. Enrichment: Repeat with the electromagnet connected to two batteries connected in series and with a six-volt battery.

PROCEDURE:
1. Obtain an iron nail, 1½-volt battery, and a 20-cm length of bell wire.
2. Wrap the wire tightly in a coil around the iron nail.
3. Connect the two ends of the wire to the battery. Attempt to pick up pins, tacks, and paper clips with the nail.
4. Remove the cover from an electric bell. Identify the electromagnet and metal striker.
5. Connect the bell and switch to a 1½-volt battery.
6. Use the switch to turn the bell on and off a few times. Observe the movement of the metal striker.

OBSERVATIONS AND DATA:

The nail is magnetic. When the bell is turned on, the electromagnet is magnetized, attracting the striker. The metal striker moves toward the electromagnet and hits the bell gong, causing the bell to ring.

QUESTIONS AND CONCLUSIONS:

1. Is the nail magnetic when the wires around it are connected to a battery? *yes*
2. How does the electromagnet operate the bell? *When magnetized, it attracts the striker.*

ADDITIONAL QUESTIONS:

An electromagnet is needed to operate the bell. When current flows through the electromagnet, it becomes magnetized and attracts the metal striker. When electric current moves through coil of wire around an iron nail, the nail becomes magnetized.

3. What happens if the wires surrounding the nail were disconnected from the dry cell? *the tacks, pins, and paper clips would drop off, because the nail would no longer be magnetized*
4. Is the magnet you made in this activity a permanent magnet? Explain. *no; When dry cell is disconnected, the magnetic qualities of the nail disappear.*
5. What happens to the electromagnet when the switch is first closed? *Electricity flows through the wires, causing the electromagnet to become magnetized.*
6. What happens to the metal striker as the electromagnet becomes magnetized? *The striker is attracted to the electromagnet and moves toward it.*
7. When striker hits gong, what happens to the electric circuit of the electromagnet? *The circuit becomes open and current stops flowing. This causes the electromagnet to lose its magnetism.*
8. What causes the striker to move back to its original position? *The striker is pulled back into place by a spring.*
9. What causes the electromagnet to again become magnetized? *When striker returns to its original position, the electric circuit is closed and electricity again flows through the electromagnet.*

ADDITIONAL ACTIVITY: Charging a Comb (section 16:4)

OBJECTIVE: To see the effects of static electricity on some common materials

CLASS TIME ALLOTMENT: 15 minutes.

MATERIALS:

pieces of paper
plastic comb
running water
wool cloth

PREPARATION NOTES:

The results of this activity depend very much on how humid the classroom is on the day of the activity. If it is too humid, static electricity will not build up enough to demonstrate the effects.

PROCEDURE:

1. Hold a plastic comb near some small pieces of paper. Observe.
2. Hold the comb near some water trickling from a faucet. Observe.
3. Rub the comb with a wool cloth.
4. Again hold the comb near small pieces of paper. Observe.
5. Rub the comb again with a wool cloth.
6. Hold comb near trickling water again. Observe.

OBSERVATIONS AND DATA:

Before rubbing, the comb attracts neither the paper nor water. After rubbing the comb with wool, the pieces of paper adhere to the comb and the stream of trickling water curves toward the comb.

QUESTIONS AND CONCLUSIONS:

Rubbing a plastic comb with wool gives the comb a static electric charge. This charge attracts paper or trickling water.
1. What kind of charge does the comb have before it is rubbed with the wool cloth? *neutral*
2. What happens after you rub the comb with the cloth? *The comb becomes negatively charged.*
3. How does the comb become charged? *Electrons are transferred from the cloth to the comb.*

ACTIVITY 16-3: Static Electricity (page 321)

OBJECTIVE: To observe how opposite and like static electric charges react

CLASS TIME ALLOTMENT: 15 minutes.

MATERIALS:

cloth, wool
glass rod
metric ruler
pith balls—2

ring stand/ring—2
rubber rod
thread

PREPARATION NOTES:

In this activity the student investigates the properties of static electricity. Tissue paper rolled into two small balls can be substituted for the pith balls. Attach each pith ball to a ring on a ring stand. Note: this activity will work best when done on days with low relative humidity.

PROCEDURE:

1. Obtain two pith balls, each attached to a thread. Suspend the balls so they are about 2 cm apart. Observe whether the balls attract or repel each other.
2. Charge a hard rubber rod with wools. Touch the rod to both pith balls. Observe whether the balls attract or repel each other.
3. Repeat Step 2 using a glass rod and wool. Observe what happens.
4. Charge one pith ball with the rubber rod and the other ball with the glass rod. Observe the result.

OBSERVATIONS AND DATA:

When pith balls are uncharged they neither attract nor repel each other. When pith balls are touched with the same charged rod, they repel one another. When each pith ball is touched with a different charged rod, the two pith balls attract each other.

QUESTIONS AND CONCLUSIONS:

1. Do uncharged pith balls attract or repel each other? Do they have the same charge? Explain.   *neither; yes, both neutral*
2. Do the balls attract or repel each other after being touched with the charged rubber rod? The charged glass rod? Explain.   *repel; both are now like-charged*
3. When each ball is touched with a differently charged rod, do they attract or repel each other? Why?   *attract; they are oppositely charged and opposite charges attract.*

ADDITIONAL QUESTIONS:

Like charges repel. Opposite charges attract.
4. Why did pith balls move apart when touched with the same rod?   *They were charged with like charges.*
5. Why did pith balls move toward each other when touched with different rods?   *They were charged with opposite charges.*

ACTIVITY 16-4: Magnetism and Electric Currents (page 326)

OBJECTIVE: To study the effects of moving a magnet through a coil of wire

CLASS TIME ALLOTMENT: 10 minutes.

MATERIALS:

bar magnet
bell wire
galvanometer

PREPARATION NOTES:

In this activity the student demonstrates that an electric current is produced when a magnet is moved back and forth through a coil of wire. If galvanometer is not available, connect the two ends of the wire together and lay the wire on the face of a compass. The compass needle will circle back and forth as the magnet is moved through the wire.

PROCEDURE:

1. Obtain a 1-m piece of wire.
2. Twist the wire into a coil having 5 loops, each with a diameter of 5 cm.
3. Attach the two ends of the wire to a galvanometer.
4. Move a bar magnet back and forth through the coil.

OBSERVATIONS AND DATA:

The galvanometer needle moves back and forth as the bar magnet is moved through the coil; the needle changes direction when the magnet changes direction. When the magnet's speed is increased, the galvanometer needle is deflected by a greater amount.

QUESTIONS AND CONCLUSIONS:

1. Is an electric current formed?   *yes*
2. How does the speed of the magnet's movement affect the quantity of electric current?   *When the magnet's speed is increased, the amount of electric current increases.*

ADDITIONAL QUESTIONS:

A magnet moving back and forth inside a coil or wire produces an alternating current inside the wire. A greater amount of current is generated when the magnet's speed is increased. NOTE: Stress to students that electricity is being produced by a moving magnetic field. The magnetic field exerts a force on electrons in the wire coil and causes them to move. This principle is called induction and is the principle by which generators and transformers operate.

3. Why is the current produced by a moving magnet called an alternating current?   *because the current changes direction when the magnet changes direction*
4. How is electricity produced by a moving magnet?   *The force produced by the magnet causes electrons to move in the wire. Moving electrons is the definition of electricity.*

ADDITIONAL ACTIVITY: Fuse Size (section 16:9)

OBJECTIVE: To observe the different size fuses (or circuit breakers) used in house and automobile circuits

CLASS TIME ALLOTMENT: 10 minutes.

MATERIALS:

fuse box in house or apartment
fuse box in automobile

PREPARATION NOTES:

This activity should be done at home.

PROCEDURE:

1. Locate the fuse box in a house or apartment.
2. List sizes of fuses (in amperes)
3. If circuit breakers are used, list amperage ratings of the circuit breakers.
4. Locate fuse box in car. If necessary, use owner's manual.
5. List sizes of the fuses.
6. Explain the difference between fuses used in house circuits and those used in automobile circuits.

OBSERVATIONS AND DATA:

House fuses or circuit breakers are rated at 15 to 30 amperes. Automobile fuses have lower ratings of from 1.5 to 15 amperes.

QUESTIONS AND CONCLUSIONS:

Automobiles use lower amperage fuses than houses. NOTE: Stress the reason fuses are used. Discuss dangers of fire resulting from poor wiring or too many appliances drawing too much current.

1. What is the purpose of a fuse or circuit breaker?   *to prevent an electric circuit from drawing too much current and overheating; overheating could cause a fire*
2. How do the voltage and the current differ between a home and an automobile?   *In a home, the voltage is higher and the current is alternating. In an automobile, the voltage is lower and the current is direct. The current in a home is higher than the current in an automobile.*
3. What is a circuit breaker?   *It is a switch that turns off if too much current passes through it. It only has to be switched back on, not replaced.*

ACTIVITY 16-5: Circuits (page 330)

OBJECTIVE: To compare a series circuit and a parallel circuit using light bulbs

CLASS TIME ALLOTMENT: 25 minutes.

MATERIALS:

battery, 1½v
bell wire
lamp receptacles/bulbs

screwdriver
switch

PREPARATION NOTES:

In this activity the student constructs a series circuit and a parallel circuit and compares the characteristics of each. It is advisable to cut the wire to the required lengths prior to class so that students need only connect the circuits as shown in the diagram.

PROCEDURE:

1. Obtain a dry cell, pieces of bell wire, a switch, a screwdriver, and several small lamp receptacles.
2. Using the screwdriver and the wire, connect three 1½ volt lamps as shown in Figure 16-22a to the dry cell.
3. Complete the wire circuit so that the lamps are lighted.
4. Unscrew one of the lamps. Observe what happens.
5. Connect the three lamps as shown in Figure 16-22b.
6. Connect the wire so the circuit is complete.
7. Unscrew one of the lamps. Observe what happens.

OBSERVATIONS AND DATA:

In a series circuit, if one lamp is disconnected, all the lamps go out. In a parallel circuit, if one lamp is disconnected, the other lamps remain lighted.

QUESTIONS AND CONCLUSIONS:

1. If all of the lamps go out when one is unscrewed, what kind of a circuit is it? *series*
2. If the other lamps remain lighted when one is unscrewed, what kind of a circuit is it? *parallel*

ADDITIONAL QUESTIONS:

Electricity stops flowing in a series circuit as soon as there is one break in the circuit. In parallel circuits, there are alternate pathways so that if the circuit is broken, only the lamps in that circuit will go out.

3. In which circuit is there more than one pathway for electric current to flow? *parallel circuit*
4. How are lights in your home wired? Explain. *In parallel; turning off one light does not cause other lights to go out.*

ADDITIONAL ACTIVITY: Conserving Electric energy (section 16:10)

OBJECTIVE: To become aware of ways to conserve energy

CLASS TIME ALLOTMENT: 20 minutes.

MATERIALS:

library
pamphlets from power companies

PREPARATION NOTES:

Discuss as many new ideas about conservation as possible. Discuss how conservation today will affect their future as consumers.

PROCEDURE:

1. Make a list of all the objects that use electricity in the home, such as light bulbs, electric appliances, and electric furnaces.
2. In a column opposite each object, write a sentence about how you could use less electricity with that object.
3. If available, read pamphlets from power companies and add to your list from Step 2 any new ideas you discover.
4. Participate in class discussion.

OBSERVATIONS AND DATA:

Answers will vary. Some observations: turn off lights when not in use; use lower wattage bulbs; insulate homes against heat loss; keep refrigerator door closed when not directly in use; defrost refrigerator regularly; turn off air conditioner when not home.

QUESTIONS AND CONCLUSIONS:

1. Why do electric companies encourage people to wash clothes during the early morning hours or late evening hours in the summer? *This practice reduces the total amount of electricity needed at any one time. During the daytime heat of summer, much electricity is needed to run appliances, especially air conditioners. If the total electricity needed at a peak time (peak amount) is kept low,*

the electric companies do not have to add new facilities and your cost for power can be kept down.

2. How could you conserve electricity when using lights in your home? *use lower wattage light bulbs; use fluorescent lights; turn off lights if not in use*

3. How could you conserve electricity when using large appliances? *defrost refrigerator regularly; wash dishes only when dishwasher is full; keep refrigerator door closed when not in direct use; turn off air conditioner when not at home; lower thermostat during winter months and raise thermostat during summer months*

CHALLENGE: APPLYING SCIENTIFIC METHODS
Exploring Magnetism

OBJECTIVE: To determine what types of materials are naturally magnetic and to discover how certain types of materials can be made magnetic

CLASS TIME ALLOTMENT: One period.

MATERIALS:

burner	paper clips, 2
cork	needle
goggles	tray
iron filings	wire cutters
magnet	

objects to be tested:

plastic bag	dime	iron bar
needle	iron filings	paper clip
brass nut	plastic comb	aluminum rod
candle	glass bottle	penny

PREPARATION NOTES:

In this activity students discover what materials are attracted to magnets and what materials are permeable to magnetic fields. Students will also magnetize an object and then try to remove its magnetic properties. Be sure that the magnet used in this activity is strong enough to attract a paper clip placed 0.5 cm below it.

PROCEDURE:

1. Test various pieces of material to see if they are attracted to a magnet. Record your observations.

2. Holding the magnet about 2 cm above a paper clip on the table, place these same materials, one at a time, between the magnet and the paper clip. Slowly lower the magnet to a distance of about 0.5 cm above the clip. Do not allow the magnet of material to touch the paper clip. Record those materials that allow a magnetic field to pass through.

3. Magnetize a needle by stroking it with a magnet as follows. Move the magnet from the eye of the needle to its point. Lift the magnet and repeat the stroke in the same direction. Repeat the stroke many times until the needle is magnetized.

4. Test the magnetism of the needle by trying to pick up several paper clips. Record the number of clips that you picked up.
5. Place the eye of the needle in a cork. Place your magnetized needle directly in a burner flame. **CAUTION:** wear goggles. Heat the needle until it glows. Let it cool. Test its magnetism on the paper clips. Record your results.
6. Unbend a paper clip. Cut the paper clip in half.
7. Magnetize one half of the paper clip by stroking it many times with the permanent magnet. NOTE: Always stroke the paper clip in the same direction. Lift the magnet between strokes.
8. Place the magnetized part of the paper clip on a tray that is sprinkled with iron filings. What happens to the filings? Record the results.
9. Remove the magnetized part of the paper clip from the tray of filings.
10. Place the part of the clip that was not magnetized in the pile of iron filings. Record your observations.
11. Cut the magnetized part of the paper clip in half. Place the two pieces of paper clip on the filings and record the results.

OBSERVATIONS AND DATA:

The materials that showed the magnetic property include the needle, iron filings, iron bar, and paper clip. The materials that allow a magnetic field to pass are the plastic bag, brass nut, candle, dime, plastic comb, glass bottle, aluminum rod, and penny.

After stroking, the needle could pick up several paper clips. After heating, no paper clips were picked up by the needle. Iron filings were attracted to the magnetized paper clip, but not the unmagnetized clip. When cut in half, both halves of the magnetized clip attracted filings.

QUESTIONS AND CONCLUSIONS:

1. (a) What materials were attracted to the magnet?   *The magnet attracted the needle, the iron filings, the iron bar, and the paper clip.*
   (b) Were all metal objects attracted to a magnet?   *No*
   (c) Which ones were not?   *The magnet did not attract the brass nut, the dime, the aluminum rod, or the penney.*
2. (a) What materials allowed magnetic fields to pass through them? *The magnetic field passed through the plastic bag, the brass nut, the candle, the dime, the plastic comb, the glass bottle, the aluminum rod, and the penny.*
   (b) Are these same materials attracted to magnets?   *no*
3. How can you destroy the magnetic properties of an object that is not a permanent magnet?   *Heating will destroy the magnetic properties of a magnet.*
4. (a) What happened to the iron filings when the magnetized paper clip was placed in the tray.   *The magnetized paper clip attracted the iron filings.*
   (b) What happened to the iron filings when the nonmagnetized paper clip was placed in the tray?   *The nonmagnetized paper clip did not attract the iron filings.*
   (c) What happened when the two halves of the magnetized paper clip were placed in the tray?   *Both halves of the magnetized paper clip attracted the filings.*

chapter 17

Nuclear Energy

ADDITIONAL ACTIVITY: X-ray Photographs (section 17:4)

OBJECTIVE: To see the effects of placing objects in the path of X rays

CLASS TIME ALLOTMENT: 15 minutes.

MATERIALS: X-ray photographs

PREPARATION NOTES:

Old X rays can often be obtained from physicians, clinics, and hospitals. X rays are used to observe the inner structure of many objects in medicine and industry.

PROCEDURE:

1. Tape X ray to a window or hold X ray up to a light source.
2. Examine the X-ray photograph.
3. Make a list of body parts you can detect.

OBSERVATIONS AND DATA:

Lists of body parts will vary. Areas that appear light are areas where X rays have been absorbed by the object and thus have not hit the photographic plate. Areas that appear dark are areas where the X rays have passed through the object.

QUESTIONS AND CONCLUSIONS:

1. Why are the bones in the X-ray photographs light in color?   *Bones absorb X rays. Thus, no X rays pass through and hit the photographic plate. Wherever X rays hit the photographic plate, it turns dark.*
2. Before the digestive tract can be examined with X rays, a person must drink barium sulfate. Why?   *Barium sulfate absorbs X rays to show an outline of the stomach and intestines on the developed film.*
3. What are some important uses for X rays?   *Answers will vary. Possible answers include studying stress flaws in metals and examining parts of the human body.*

ACTIVITY 17-1: Measuring Radiation (page 347)

OBJECTIVE: To use a Geiger counter to measure radiation

CLASS TIME ALLOTMENT: 20 minutes.

MATERIALS:

aluminum sheet	Geiger counter	lead sheet
clock or watch	glass sheet	mantle from camp lantern

PREPARATION NOTES:

In this activity the student, using a Geiger counter, measures radiation from a lantern mantle and investigates the effect of glass, aluminum, and lead on radiation. If a Geiger counter is not available, it may be possible to borrow one from the high school physics department.

PROCEDURE:

1. Place a Geiger counter on the table and plug it into an electric outlet. Turn the counter on and record the number of clicks per minute.
2. Place a mantle from a camp lantern 15 cm from the counter tube. Record the number of clicks per minute.
3. Place a sheet of glass between the mantle and the Geiger counter. Record the number of clicks per minute.
4. Place a piece of aluminum between the mantle and the counter. Record the number of clicks per minute.
5. Put a lead sheet in front of the mantle and count the clicks per minutes.

OBSERVATIONS AND DATA:

CLICKS/MINUTE	NO SHIELD	GLASS SHEET	ALUMINUM SHEET	LEAD SHEET

When different materials are placed in the path of the radioactive source, the clicks per minute decrease: (1) slightly with glass; (2) more with aluminum; and (3) almost completely with lead.

QUESTIONS AND CONCLUSIONS:

1. What is the radiation that occurs naturally in the environment called?   *background radiation*
2. Is the number of clicks per minute different when the lantern mantle is placed near the counter tube? Why?   *yes; the mantle contains radioactive nuclides*
3. What effect does placing glass between the mantle and Geiger counter have? Explain.   *The clicks per minute decrease; glass stops some of the radiation.*
4. What effect does placing aluminum between the mantle and Geiger counter have? Explain.   *The clicks per minute decrease further; aluminum is a better shield than glass.*
5. What effect does placing lead between the mantle and Geiger counter have?   *The lowest amount of clicks is heard.*
6. Why are lead sheets used to provide protection against radiation?   *Lead sheet is a better shield than aluminum. Lead blocks the radiation.*

ADDITIONAL ACTIVITY: Chain Reaction with Dominoes (section 17:6)

OBJECTIVE: To study the effect produced in a chain reaction

CLASS TIME ALLOTMENT: 10 minutes.

MATERIALS:
dominoes—15

PREPARATION NOTES:
In this activity, students construct a model of a chain reaction. They then compare a reaction in which all the particles are regularly arranged with one in which the particles are random.

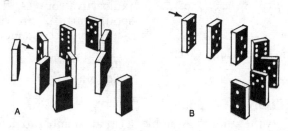

FIGURE 17-1

PROCEDURE:
1. Predict what will happen if the first domino in arrangement A is pushed in the direction of the arrow.
2. Repeat Step 1 for arrangement B.
3. Collect 15 dominoes and test the predictions you made in Steps 1 and 2 by building the arrangements of dominoes shown in the figure above.

OBSERVATIONS AND DATA:
In both arrangements, once the domino in front falls, it causes the complete set behind it to fall. With arrangement A, there are instances of one domino knocking over two other dominoes.

QUESTIONS AND CONCLUSIONS:
1. Which arrangement of dominoes produces a chain reaction? *both* Explain. *In arrangement B, the first domino hits the second, the second the third, and this process continues until all dominoes are knocked down. In arrangement A, the first domino hits two other dominoes. These two dominoes hit three others and the process continues until all dominoes have fallen. A chain reaction proceeds by itself once it is started.*
2. Which arrangement is like fission inside a nuclear reactor? *arrangement A.* Explain. *In A, one domino can hit two other dominoes, expanding the chain reaction. This is similar to a fast moving neutron hitting a uranium nucleus and producing 2 neutrons, then four, and so on.*

CHALLENGE: APPLYING SCIENTIFIC METHODS
Detecting Alpha and Beta Particles

OBJECTIVE: To identify alpha and beta particles by their condensation trails.

CLASS TIME ALLOTMENT: One period.

MATERIALS:

aluminum pan, painted black
cardboard sheet, 30 cm × 30 cm
caulking compound and applicator
clay
construction paper, black, cut to fit
   exterior of container
dry ice, 20 cm × 20 cm × 2 cm
ethanol
forceps
glass or plastic sheet, clear, 20 cm ×
   20 cm

dropper
plastic food storage container,
   round, 15 cm diameter, bottom
   removed
projector or high-intensity light
   source
radioactive sources, alpha and beta
sponge strip, 2 cm wide, cut to fit
   interior of container
tape
tongs
white glue

PREPARATION NOTES:

In this activity the student assembles a cloud chamber to detect alpha and beta particles produced by a radioactive source. Radioactive sources of alpha and beta particles are available from most scientific supply houses. You may wish to conduct this activity as a demonstration.

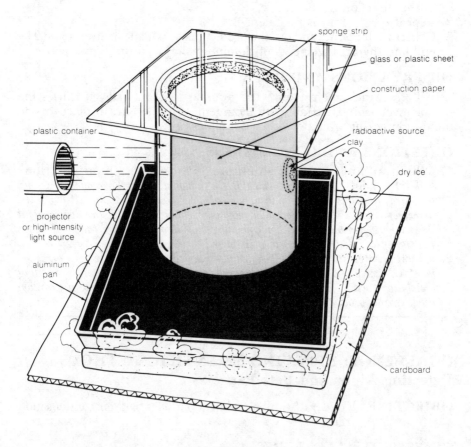

FIGURE 17-2

PROCEDURE:

Part A: Assembling the Cloud Chamber

1. Glue the sponge strip to the inside of the container near the upper rim. The strip must extend along the entire rim.
2. Attach the alpha source to the inside of the container with clay. The source should be about 5 cm from the upper rim. **CAUTION:** Use forceps to handle the radioactive source.
3. Tape the construction paper to the outside of the container. Leave an opening 10 cm wide opposite the radioactive source.
4. Cover the bottom rim of the container with caulking compound and securely attach the rim to the aluminum pan.
5. Using the dropper, soak the sponge with ethanol.
6. Cover the upper rim of the container with caulking compound and securely attach the glass or plastic sheet.
7. Place the dry ice on a sheet of cardboard. **CAUTION:** Use tongs to handle the dry ice.
8. Place the aluminum pan of the cloud chamber on the dry ice.
9. Illuminate the inside of the chamber with the projector or high-intensity light source.

Part B: Observing the Tracks of the Particles

1. Allow the ethanol to evaporate and cool for several minutes.
2. Adjust the light source so that the small trails of clouds can be seen.
3. Observe the tracks of the alpha particles.
4. Record your observations by drawing diagrams of the tracks.
5. Carefully remove the glass or plastic sheet and replace the alpha particle source with the beta particle source. **CAUTION:** Use forceps to handle the radioactive sources.
6. Add more ethanol to the sponge and replace the glass or plastic sheet.
7. After a few minutes, small clouds will appear. Observe the tracks of the beta particles.
8. Record your observations by drawing diagrams of the tracks.

OBSERVATIONS AND DATA:

The alpha particle tracks should appear somewhat fuzzy, long, and fairly straight. The beta particle tracks should appear fine, short, and somewhat circular.

QUESTIONS AND CONCLUSIONS:

1. How do the widths of the tracks of the alpha particles compare to the widths of the tracks of the beta particles?   *The tracks of the alpha particles appear wider than those of the beta particles. (The alpha particle is larger and carries a greater charge than does the beta particle. These factors cause greater condensation resulting in a wider track.)*
2. How do the lengths of the tracks of the alpha particles compare to the length of the tracks of the beta particles?   *The tracks of the alpha particles are longer than those of the beta particles. (The alpha particle has greater mass than the beta particle. The greater mass gives the alpha particle more momentum.)*
3. How does the straightness of the tracks compare?   *The tracks of the alpha particles are straighter than those of the beta particles. (The greater momentum of the alpha particle causes it to be less deflected than the beta particle.)*

UNIT FIVE

Astronomy

chapter 18

Astronomy and the Moon

ACTIVITY 18-1: Making a Refracting Telescope (page 361)

OBJECTIVE: To construct and use a simple refracting telescope

CLASS TIME ALLOTMENT: 30 minutes.

MATERIALS:

cardboard mailing tube—2
convex lens—2, with focal lengths
  of 20 cm and 2.5 cm

glue
scissors
stiff cardboard

PREPARATION NOTES:

In this activity the student constructs a refracting telescope using two convex lenses. Explain the meaning of focal length as the distance from the lens to the point of principal focus where light rays converge to a point. Caution students to use the glue sparingly and not to get glue on the lenses.

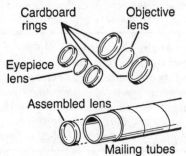

FIGURE 18-1

PROCEDURE:

1. Obtain two convex lenses with focal lengths of about 20 cm and 2.5 cm. Also obtain a piece of stiff cardboard and two mailing tubes. One tube should slide inside the other. The short focal length lens will be the eyepiece lens. The other lens will be the objective lens.
2. Cut two cardboard disks for each lens. The diameters of the disks should be the same as the inside diameters of the tubes.

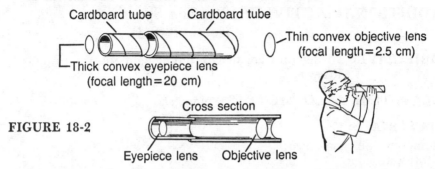

FIGURE 18-2

3. Cut a circle in each disk with a diameter slightly smaller than the diameter of each lens. These rings will hold the lenses in place (Figure 18-1).
4. Apply a thin film of glue to each ring. Then glue the rings together around each lens. Avoid getting glue on the centers of the lenses.
5. Glue one disk in one end of each tube.
6. Slide the small tube inside the other.
7. Look at a distant object through the telescope. **CAUTION:** Never look at the sun with the unaided eye or with a telescope. Severe eye damage may result. To focus the telescope, slide the small tube in and out of the large tube.

OBSERVATIONS AND DATA:

The image is inverted. The clarity of the image decreases as the length of the tube changes. To view an object clearly, the real image formed at the focal point of the objective lens must appear at the focal point of the eyepiece.

QUESTIONS AND CONCLUSIONS:

1. Is the image upright or inverted?   *inverted*
2. What happens to the image as you slide the tube. Why?   *The clarity of the image decreases as the length of the tube changes. To view an object clearly, the real image formed at the focal point of the objective lens must appear at the focal point of the eyepiece.*

ADDITIONAL QUESTIONS:

3. How is the telescope you made like those made by early astronomers?   *In principle and construction they are the same, but the materials are very different.*
4. Name one improvement that could be made to your telescope design.   *bigger or better lenses, construction materials, mounting stand, etc.*
5. Could a telescope be made that would use additional lenses or one that could be adjusted for better focus? Draw or describe a plan.   *yes; one that may function like a folding scope*

6. What do you predict would happen by changing the following variables?
   (a) size of lenses   *The larger size lens would collect more light until lens reached the size where its weight could not be supported.*
   (b) focal length of lenses   *Different magnifications are gained.*
   (c) concave rather than convex lenses   *Concave lens will reduce the size of the image and it will be right-side up.*

ADDITIONAL ACTIVITY: Shoebox Spectroscope (section 18:3)

OBJECTIVE: To demonstrate that different light sources produce a different spectrum

CLASS TIME ALLOTMENT: 25 minutes.

MATERIALS:
aluminum foil, small piece
fluorescent lamp
plastic diffraction grating, small piece (available from scientific supply house)
ruler
scissors/knife
shoebox
unfrosted incandescent light bulb

PREPARATION NOTES:

In this activity, students study the spectra produced by different light sources.

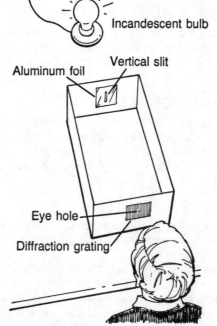

FIGURE 18-3

PROCEDURE:

1. Obtain a shoebox and a small piece of plastic diffraction grating.
2. At one end of the box, cut a circle with a 1 cm diameter.
3. Tape the piece of grating across this opening.
4. Cut a circle with a 1 cm diameter at the opposite end of the box.
5. Cover the opening with a piece of aluminum foil in which a vertical slit has been cut with a sharp knife. The slit should be parallel to the grating pattern in the piece of plastic diffraction grating.
6. Place the cover on the box.
7. Aim the slit at an unfrosted incandescent light bulb.
8. With one eye, look into the box through the grating and observe the color spectrum.
9. Repeat the procedure with a flourescent lamp. Compare the two spectra you observe.

OBSERVATIONS AND DATA:

The spectrum is different for the two types of light sources. The light from the incandescent bulb produced a rainbow of colors when beamed through the spectroscope. The fluorescent lamp produced bands of violet and blue.

QUESTIONS AND CONCLUSIONS:

1. What did the spectrum look like for (a) the incandescent bulb; and (b) the fluorescent bulb?   *all spectrum colors with the incandescent bulb; violet and blue with the fluorescent bulb*
2. How were the two spectra alike?   *Both had blue and green.*   How were they different?   *Incandescent also had red, yellow, orange.*
3. Would the spectrum be different for other sources of light?   *Yes, each light source has a different spectrum.*
4. What would the spectrum of visible light from the sun be like?   *a rainbow*

ACTIVITY 18-2: The Distance to the Moon (page 366)

OBJECTIVE: To calculate the approximate distance from the earth to the moon

CLASS TIME ALLOTMENT: 15 minutes.

MATERIALS:

meter stick   metric ruler   pencil

PREPARATION NOTES:

In this activity the student calculates the approximate distance from Earth to the moon. The measurement is made by an indirect method using proportions. It is recommended that this activity be done as an out of class assignment. Review the procedure and explain the use of the equation to determine the distance in kilometers to the moon. Use the value of 3476 km for the moon's diameter. Show students how to measure the diameter in millimeters with a metric ruler.

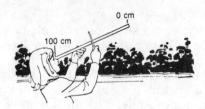

FIGURE 18-4

PROCEDURE:

1. Go outside with a pencil and a meter stick on a night when there is a full moon (complete circle).
2. Hold the meter stick just below one eye and close your other eye.
3. Sight along the meter stick toward the moon.
4. Hold the pencil beside the meter stick and move it until its width just blocks your view of the moon.
5. Record the distance in millimeters from your eye to the pencil.
6. Measure the width of the pencil in millimeters and record it. Determine the distance to the moon using this equation.

$$\frac{\text{diameter of moon (km)}}{\text{diameter of pencil (mm)}} = \frac{\text{distance to moon (km)}}{\text{distance to pencil (mm)}}$$

OBSERVATIONS AND DATA:

Figures on the distance from eye to pencil and width of pencil will vary among students. Computed distance to the moon will vary among students.

QUESTIONS AND CONCLUSIONS:

1. How close is your answer to the distance given in the text?   *In this proportion, the distance varies directly with the diameter. Because this method is crude, a student's reasonably close answer will be "in the ballpark," meaning an approximation.*

ADDITIONAL QUESTIONS:

2. What answer did you calculate?   *Answers will vary.*
3. Why do you suppose that your answer is different from the distance to the moon given in the text?   *The distance varies directly with the diameter of the pencil. Because it is difficult to measure the pencil's diameter accurately, the distance will be a rough approximation.*
4. Can you think of another way to determine the average distance to the moon?   *bouncing radar, light waves, or laser beams off the moon and calculating the distance using the time it takes for the waves or beams to return to Earth*
5. Why is the moon's distance reported as an average distance?   *It is an average because the distance continually changes due to the moon's elliptical orbit around Earth.*

ADDITIONAL ACTIVITY: Moon Size (section 18:6)

OBJECTIVE: To determine if the moon changes size as it rises

CLASS TIME ALLOTMENT: 10 minutes.

MATERIALS: coins (different sizes)

PREPARATION NOTES:

In this activity, students compare the size of the moon at different times during the evening. It is recommended that this activity be done at home.

PROCEDURE:

1. View a full moon when it is just above the horizon.
2. Hold different size coins at arm's length until you find one that just covers the moon.
3. Repeat the procedure later in the evening when the moon is higher.

OBSERVATIONS AND DATA:

The moon appeared larger when it was just above the horizon and smaller when it was high in the sky. At both times, the same coin would just cover the moon. Note that only the moon's apparent size changes. Its actual size remains the same.

QUESTIONS AND CONCLUSIONS:

1. What size coin covered the moon?   *a quarter*
2. What did you observe when the moon had risen higher in the sky?   *The moon appeared to be smaller.*
3. What size coin was needed to cover it later in the evening?   *smaller coin*
4. What causes the moon to appear smaller as it rises?   *The moon appears smaller due to the optical illusion created by the increased distance from the horizon.*

ADDITIONAL ACTIVITY: Tracking the Moon's Rise (section 18:6)

OBJECTIVE: To demonstrate that the moon rises at a different time each night

CLASS TIME ALLOTMENT: 10 minutes.

MATERIALS: binoculars (optional)   paper
                            newspaper (source of moonrise and   pencil
                                moonset times)

PREPARATION NOTES:

In this activity, students observe the time of moonrise for several consecutive nights. Students should observe that the moon rises 50 to 51 minutes later each night, and that less of the moon is visible each night. It is recommended that this activity be assigned as an out of class assignment.

PROCEDURE:

1. Draw a chart like the one shown to record your sightings.
2. In a newspaper, locate the date and time of the next full moon. On this day begin watching for the moon after sunset.
3. On your chart, record the day and exact minute you see the moon rise.
4. For one week, record the date and time of moonrise.
5. Draw the different shapes of the moon.
6. Use information from the newspaper to complete the moonset columns.

DATE	MOON RISE	MOON SET	MOON SHAPE

OBSERVATIONS AND DATA:

The student's recorded time of moonrise should be close to the newspaper recorded time. Each night moonrise was about 50 or 51 minutes later. Less of the moon was visible each night.

QUESTIONS AND CONCLUSIONS:

1. Do your observations of moonrise agree with the information given in the newspaper? *should agree fairly well*
2. If your observed moonrise time is not the same, why do you suppose it is different? *Your location compared to the official viewing location may differ or there may be a difference in clocks.*
3. What Earth motion is involved in the time of moonrise? *rotation*
4. Is moonrise the same each night? *No, the moon rises later each night.*
5. How much later is moonrise each night? *50 to 51 minutes*
6. If the moon rose at 6:00 p.m. on Monday, what time would it rise the following Sunday? *about 5 hours later, or 11:00 p.m.*

ACTIVITY 18-3: Moon Watch (page 369)

OBJECTIVE: To record the positions and shapes of the moon

CLASS TIME ALLOTMENT: 10 minutes.

MATERIALS:

almanac or daily newspaper
paper, 100 cm × 80 cm
pencil

PREPARATION NOTES:

In this activity the student observes the phases of the moon by recording the positions and shapes of the moon. Have students begin the activity at the start of a new synodic cycle. When the moon is halfway between new and first quarter, it will be located 45° to the east of the sun. It will appear to follow the sun by three hours throughout the day. The moon will set about three hours after sunset. Have students continue their observations for about the next two weeks. In one half of a synodic month (about 15 days) the moon will follow the sun by 12 hours. Consequently the full moon must rise at sunset and set at sunrise.

PROCEDURE:

1. Draw a large half-circle on the paper. Divide the half circle on the paper into 14 equal parts. Label east and west at opposite ends of the half-circle.
2. Take the diagram outside and look south. Draw some landmarks, such as trees and buildings, on the bottom of the half-circle.
3. Two days after new moon, begin observing the moon. Sketch the exact position and shape of the moon on your diagram. Date the sketch.
4. On the same day, begin to record the moonrise and moonset times. Use the almanac for moonset times.
5. Sketch the position and shape of the moon every night for two weeks at about the same time each day. Date each sketch. Leave a dated space on your diagram if you cannot see the moon.
6. Record the moonrise and moonset times every day for two weeks.

OBSERVATIONS AND DATA:

DATE	MOONRISE TIME	MOONSET TIME

The delay of moonrise can vary from about one half hour to over an hour. Variation depends on the time of the year and the latitude. In northern latitudes, the delay is shorter in the fall and longer in the spring.

QUESTIONS AND CONCLUSIONS:

1. According to your diagram, in what direction did the moon travel?   *west to east*
2. Where is the moon on your diagram after two weeks?   *toward the left*
3. What was the moon's shape?   *near full moon*
4. How much later was moonrise each night?   *about 51 minutes later each night*
5. If the moon rose at 6:00 p.m. on Monday, at what time would it rise the following Sunday?   *11:06 p.m.*

ACTIVITY 18-4: Solar Eclipse (page 372)

OBJECTIVE: To simulate a solar eclipse in order to develop an understanding of the cause of an eclipse

CLASS TIME ALLOTMENT: 10 minutes.

MATERIALS:

lamp receptacle/bulb   meter stick
marble

PREPARATION NOTES:

In this activity the student simulates a solar eclipse in order to develop an understanding of the cause of an eclipse. Compare the marble and the bulb to the sun and the moon, which they represent.

PROCEDURE:

Place a bare, lighted electric bulb at a distance of 4 m from you. Close one eye and hold a marble at arm's length in front of you. Line up the marble with the bare bulb. Move the marble closer to your eye.

OBSERVATIONS AND DATA:

Students should observe that when the marble is moved closer to their eyes, it appears to become larger. When the lamp was far away, the marble blocked out the light at some point closer to the eye than an arm's length. When the lamp was close, the marble was too small to block out much light.

QUESTIONS AND CONCLUSIONS:

A solar eclipse occurs when the moon (marble) passes between the earth (eye) and the sun (lamp). Because of the great distance between the moon and sun, the much smaller moon is able to block the light from the earth.
1. What happens when the marble is moved closer to your eye? *The marble appears to become larger as it is moved toward the eye, eventually blocking out the light from the bulb.*
2. How is this activity similar to a solar eclipse? *During the solar eclipse, the moon, which appears to be the same size as the sun, blocks the sun's light.*
3. What does the marble represent? the bare light bulb? *The marble represents the moon and the bulb represents the sun.*

ADDITIONAL QUESTIONS:

4. As you move the marble closer to your eye, does it reach a point where it blocks out the light of the lamp? *yes, when the lamp is far away*
5. What do you observe when you repeat the procedure closer to the lamp? *Close up, the marble is too small to cut off the lamp's light.*
6. Draw the relationship of the marble, lamp, and your eye to show how a solar eclipse occurs.

CHALLENGE: APPLYING SCIENTIFIC METHODS
Eclipse Formation

OBJECTIVE: To determine why different eclipses occur

CLASS TIME ALLOTMENT: 20 minutes.

MATERIALS:

pencil   compass
colored pencils, one dark color, one light color   metric ruler
ruler

PREPARATION NOTES:

In this activity, the student draws diagrams to illustrate the conditions that must be present in order for solar and lunar eclipses to occur. Explain to students that as the earth revolves around the sun, the earth's shadow is cast off into space. The shadow forms on the side of earth away from the sun. The shadow consists of two parts. The umbra is the total dark shadow. The penumbra is the partial, lighter shadow. A lunar eclipse occurs when the moon is in the earth's shadow. A solar eclipse occurs when the earth is in the moon's shadow.

PROCEDURE:

1. Using the compass, draw a circle with a diameter of 5 cm at the left edge of your paper. This circle represents the sun. To the right draw a second circle whose center is 15.25 cm from the center of the sun. The diameter of the second circle should be 2.5 cm. The second circle represents the earth. Draw a third circle to the right of the earth. The third circle's center should be 2.5 cm from the center of the earth's circle. The diameter of the third circle should be 2 cm. The third circle represents the moon.
2. Draw a straight line from the top edge of the sun to across the top edge of the earth. Extend the line far behind the earth. In the same manner, draw a line from the bottom edge of the sun to the bottom edge of the earth.
3. Using a dark colored pencil, color in the shadow formed behind the earth where the sun's light does not reach. Label this area umbra.
4. Draw straight lines from the top edge of the sun to the bottom edge of the earth and from the bottom edge of the sun to the top edge of the earth. Extend these lines behind the earth. Label the two shadows formed the penumbra, and color them with the lighter colored pencil.
5. Using your compass and ruler, draw circles representing the sun and the earth as you did in Step 1. Then draw the moon to the left of the earth, using the same dimensions that you used in Step 1.
6. Draw straight lines from the top edge of the sun to the top edge of the moon and from the bottom edge of the sun to the bottom edge of the moon. Extend both lines to the earth and label this area the umbra.
7. Using the same color as in Step 3, color the umbra between the moon and the Earth.
8. Draw straight lines from the top edge of the sun to the bottom edge of the moon and from the bottom edge of the sun to the top edge of the moon. Extend both lines to the earth. Label the two shadows formed penumbra.
9. Using the same color as in Step 4, color these shadows.

OBSERVATIONS AND DATA:

Student diagrams should resemble those shown below.

FIGURE 18-5

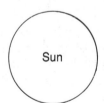

Moon

Earth

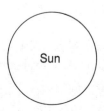

Moon

Earth

QUESTIONS AND CONCLUSIONS:

1. (a) Which type of eclipse is represented by the first diagram you drew?   *a lunar eclipse*
   (b) Explain what is happening in the first diagram.   *The moon is passing through the earth's shadow.*
2. (a) Which type of eclipse is represented by the second diagram you drew?   *a solar eclipse*
   (b) Explain what is happening in the second diagram.   *The earth is passing through the moon's shadow.*
3. What is the difference between an umbra and a penumbra.   *The umbra is the total shadow, the penumbra is a partial shadow.*

---

chapter 19

Our Solar System

ACTIVITY 19-1: An Ellipse (page 383)

OBJECTIVE: To investigate the properties of an ellipse

CLASS TIME ALLOTMENT: 30 minutes

MATERIALS:
cardboard—large stiff piece
metric ruler
pencil
string—40 cm
thumbtacks—2

PREPARATION NOTES:

In this activity the student investigates the properties of an ellipse. The eccentricity or elongation of the ellipse is determined by the distance between the foci.

PROCEDURE:

1. Stick two thumbtacks 14 cm apart into a piece of stiff cardboard.
2. Tie the ends of a 40 cm piece of string together to form a loop.
3. Place the loop around the tacks and place your pencil inside the loop.
4. Draw a figure keeping the string tight at all times.
5. Move the tacks closer together and draw another ellipse.
6. Remove one tack and draw a third figure.

OBSERVATIONS AND DATA:

The first figure is oval-shaped (elliptical). The second figure is more circular. The third figure is circular. Its distance from a fixed central point is always the same.

QUESTIONS AND CONCLUSIONS:

An ellipse has the shape of a flattened circle. It is formed by a path around to points (foci). A circle results when there is only one focus.
1. Describe the first figure.   *oval-shaped*
2. How does the second figure compare to the first one?   *It is more circular.*
3. How is the third figure different from the other two?   *its distance is fixed, central point is always the same*

ADDITIONAL QUESTIONS:

4. How can the shape of the figures be changed?   *by changing the position of the tacks or length of the string*
5. How does this activity relate to the motion of the planets?   *Planets have elliptical orbits.*
6. Why aren't the planets' orbits circular?   *If the sun's gravity were the only force acting on the planets, their orbits would be circles. However, the sun's gravity is somewhat counteracted by the planets' inertia. Inertia is the tendency of moving objects to keep moving in straight lines. Thus the orbits are elliptical.*

ACTIVITY 19-2: Period of Revolution (page 389)

OBJECTIVE: To compare the time of revolution of an object with its distance from the center of revolution.

CLASS TIME ALLOTMENT: 30 minutes.

MATERIALS:

meter stick or metric ruler
one-hole rubber stopper
string—150 cm
watch or clock with second hand

PREPARATION NOTES:

In this activity the student compares the time of revolution of an object with its distance from the center of revolution. **CAUTION:** Be certain that students have sufficient clearance when swinging the stopper to prevent damage and injury. This activity demonstrates Kepler's third law.

PROCEDURE:

1. Obtain a one-hole rubber stopper and a 150 cm piece of string.
2. Tie the string securely to the stopper.
3. Hold the string at a distance of 50 cm from the stopper and twirl the stopper in an orbit around your head. Twirl the stopper fast enough to keep it level. **CAUTION:** Do not hit anyone or anything with the stopper.
4. Have a partner time how long it takes for the stopper to make 10 revolutions around your head. Divide the time by 10 to find the time of one revolution.
5. Hold the string 75 cm from the stopper and repeat Steps 3 and 4.
6. Hold the string 100 cm from the stopper and repeat Steps 3 and 4.

OBSERVATIONS AND DATA:

DISTANCE	TIME
50 cm	
75 cm	
100 cm	

Your head represents the sun, and stopper represents a planet. The time of one revolution in the second trial was longer than that in the first trial. The third trial was longer than the first and second.

QUESTIONS AND CONCLUSIONS:
1. What in space does your head represent? *the sun* The stopper? *a planet*
2. How does the time of one revolution in the second trial compare to the first trial? *longer*
3. How does the time of the third trial compare to the other two? *longer*
4. How does this activity demonstrate Kepler's third law? *the farther the sun, the longer the period of revolution*
5. How does this activity provide evidence that Mercury has the shortest period of revolution for the planets? *Mercury is closest to the sun.*

CHALLENGE: APPLYING SCIENTIFIC METHODS
Formation of Craters

OBJECTIVE: To experimentally form craters and observe their shapes

CLASS TIME ALLOTMENT: 20 minutes.

MATERIALS:
aluminum pan
floodlight (or unshaded bulb)
glass marble
meter stick
newspaper

ruler, metric
sand, dry
steel ball
thread (or string), 1.5 m
tape

PREPARATION NOTES:
In this activity students use a steel ball and a glass marble to form craters in dry sand and then compare the sizes and shapes formed. Using a floodlight or unshaded bulb, students then observe the craters at different angles. In order for this activity to work well, the sand must not be packed. Students should be able to conclude that the size of the crater formed depends on the mass of the object and the speed at which the object hits the surface.

PROCEDURE:
1. Place the newspaper on the floor with the pan in the center.
2. Pour sand into the pan to a depth of about 4 cm.
3. Smooth the sand over with your hand. Do not pack the sand.
4. Tape one end of the thread to a steel ball.
5. From a height of 50 cm, drop the ball into the sand.

6. Using the string, gently lift the ball straight out of the sand.
7. Observe in detail the shape of the crater formed and record the diameter of the crater.
8. Shine the floodlight at different angles toward the crater. Carefully observe the different shadows that form.
9. Measure the diameter of the crater and record.
10. Smooth the sand over, being careful not to pack it down.
11. Drop the steel ball from a height of 1 m. Remove it by pulling straight up on the string. Observe the crater at different angles with the floodlight. Record the crater diameter.
12. Repeat Steps 4 to 11 using a glass marble instead of the steel ball. Record all results.

OBSERVATIONS AND DATA:

Student results will vary with the diameter of the object and the care taken in removing it from the sand. Results will also vary with the type of sand used.

QUESTIONS AND CONCLUSIONS:

1. Was sand thrown out of the crater when the steel ball and glass marble hit the surface?   *Sand was thrown out when both the steel ball and glass marble hit the surface.*
2. Was there a raised rim around the crater?   *yes*
3. About how many times greater was the diameter of the crater
   (a) than the steel ball?   *Student answers will vary.*
   (b) than the marble?   *Student answers will vary.*
4. (a) Which made a larger crater, the steel ball or marble?   *steel ball*
   (b) Why?   *The Steel ball has more mass than the glass marble and therefore had more momentum.*
5. Did increasing the height dropped to the sand affect the size of the crater formed by the steel ball and marble?   *Yes, increasing the height caused the size of the craters to increase.*
6. Having observed your craters at different angles with a floodlight, explain why some areas of the moon may appear as dark stained areas.   *These areas are shadows cast by the rims of the craters.*

---

chapter 20

Stars and Galaxies

ACTIVITY 20-1: Light and Distance (page 411)

OBJECTIVE: To investigate the inverse square law as it applies to light

CLASS TIME ALLOTMENT: 15 minutes.

MATERIALS:

lamp receptacle/socket
light bulb—25 watt
light meter
meter stick or metric ruler

PREPARATION NOTES:

In this activity the student will investigate the inverse square law as it applies to light. The activity may also be used to demonstrate apparent brightness. For the best results, you should make the room as dark as possible, and have two students do this activity as a demonstration. The teacher can furnish students with the distance and light meter readings as they are obtained. The ASA setting on the light meter should be at 50 for this activity.

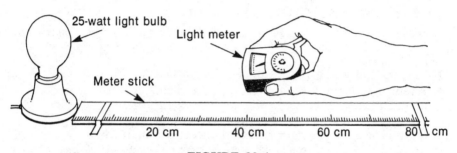

FIGURE 20-1

PROCEDURE:

1. Tape a meter stick flat on a table top.
2. Mount a 25-watt light bulb at the zero end of the meter stick. The bulb should be as close to the meter stick as possible.
3. Totally darken the room and light the bulb.
4. Place the light meter at the 20 cm mark on the meter stick. Record the distance and the light meter reading. NOTE: Light meter readings should be recorded in luxes. If the light meter expresses readings as EV numbers, refer to the Conversion Table to determine luxes. Inform students that luxes are units for measuring light intensity.
5. Double the distance between the light meter and light bulb by placing the meter at the 40 cm mark. Record the distance and light meter reading.
6. Triple and quadruple the distance by placing the light meter at the 60 cm and 80 cm marks. Record the distance and light meter reading at each mark.
7. Determine the mathematical relationship between light intensity and distance. Refer to the sample data in the Data Table. NOTE: This data was obtained by actual experimentation. It is not exact. However, it is accurate enough to determine a relationship.

OBSERVATIONS AND DATA:

CONVERSION TABLE

EV	LUX
—3	.7
—2	1.4
—1	2.8
0	5.5
1	11
2	22
3	44
4	88
5	175
6	350

DISTANCE FROM LIGHT	LIGHT METER READING IN LUXES	
	SAMPLE	ACTIVITY
20 cm	4150	
40 cm	1050	
60 cm	460	
80 cm	262.5	

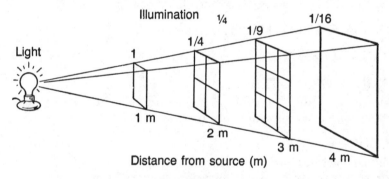

FIGURE 20-2

When the distance between the light and light meter was doubled (from 20 cm to 40 cm), light intensity decreased by ¼. When the distance was tripled (from 20 cm to 60 cm), light intensity decreased by ⅑. At four times the distance (from 20 cm to 80 cm), light intensity decreased by ¹/₁₆. The relationship between distance and light intensity can be expressed by the fraction: 1/square of how many times distance is increased ($\frac{1}{2}^2 = \frac{1}{4}$; $\frac{1}{3}^2 = \frac{1}{9}$; $\frac{1}{4}^2 = \frac{1}{16}$).

QUESTIONS AND CONCLUSIONS:

As distance increases, light intensity decreases in definite proportion.
1. Where was the light intensity greatest?   *nearest the source*

2. What is the mathematical relationship between light intensity (amount of light) and distance? *A fraction of one over the square of how many times the distance is increased.*

$$Illumination = \frac{Intensity}{(Distance)^2}$$

ADDITIONAL QUESTIONS:

3. How can this principle apply to light that is generated by a star? *Its intensity diminishes according to this law.*
4. What would be the effect of the sun's light intensity on the earth if the earth were closer to the sun? *greater* Further from the sun? *smaller*
5. Show the mathematical relationship between light intensity and distance, if the distance is increased five times? $1/_5{}^2 = 1/_{25}$
6. What does the answer to question 5 tell you about the brightness of the light at five times the distance? *The light is only $1/_{25}$ as bright at five times the distance.*
7. Why is intensity lower at a greater distance? *Light from the source has more chance to spread out. There is less light to strike a given surface farther away.*

ADDITIONAL ACTIVITY: See Parallax Yourself (section 20:1)

OBJECTIVE: To observe the principle of parallax

CLASS TIME ALLOTMENT: 5 minutes.

MATERIALS: pencil

PREPARATION NOTES:

This activity demonstrates the principle of parallax by using a pencil. It should be done as an introduction to parallax.

PROCEDURE:

1. Hold a pencil in front of you at arm's length.
2. Look at it with your left eye, but close your right eye.
3. Line up the pencil with some object in the background.
4. Without moving the pencil or your hand, open your right eye and close your left eye.
5. Again look at the same object in the background.
6. Record your observations.

OBSERVATIONS AND DATA:

The pencil appeared to have moved when observed with the right eye.

QUESTIONS AND CONCLUSIONS:

1. What did you observe? *The pencil appears to move.*
2. Does the same thing occur if the object is some distance away? *Yes, but a smaller amount of movement is shown.*
3. Describe what parallax is. *Parallax is the apparent change of position of an object against a background.*

ACTIVITY 20-2: Parallax (page 412)

OBJECTIVE: To observe a relationship between distance from an object and parallax

CLASS TIME ALLOTMENT: 20 minutes.

MATERIALS:

chalk and chalkboard   pencil
meter stick   ring stand and clamp

PROCEDURE:

1. Put twelve vertical lines, 10 cm apart, on the chalkboard. Number them in order (1-12) from left to right.
2. Clamp a pencil to the ring stand and place it between you and the chalkboard.
3. Use the following method to find the parallax of the pencil. Stand 1 m from the pencil. Use your left eye to observe the pencil's position against the lines on the chalkboard.
4. Without moving, repeat the observations with your right eye. The apparent change in postition of the pencil is the parallax. For example, if the pencil is aligned with line 8 on the chalkboard when seen with your right eye and aligned with line 4 when seen with your left eye, the parallax is 4 (8 − 4 = 4).
5. Repeat Steps 3 and 4 at 2 m, 3 m, and 4 m from the pencil.
6. Record the amount of parallax in each case.

OBSERVATIONS AND DATA:

The closer the object (pencil), the greater distance of parallax.

QUESTIONS AND CONCLUSIONS:

1. What is the relationship between the amount of parallax and your distance from the pencil? *The greater the distance, the less the parallax.*

ADDITIONAL QUESTIONS:

2. Do you think this relationship will hold true when great distances are involved? *Yes*
3. Can parallax be used to measure the distances to stars far away? *No. Parallax can only be used to measure distance to close stars. This method works for stars that are within 300 light-years of Earth.*
4. How can parallax apply in the study of astronomy? *Distances to some close stars and planets can be calculated by determining their parallax.*
5. What, besides distance from the object, can affect the amount of parallax? *the distance between the two viewing objects (Student results in this activity will vary due to variation in the distance between each individual's eyes.)*

CHALLENGE: APPLYING SCIENTIFIC METHODS
Motions of the Stars

OBJECTIVE: To construct an astrolabe and use it to measure the angles of the stars above the horizon

CLASS TIME ALLOTMENT: 15 minutes to construct astrolabe.

MATERIALS:

compass
drinking straw
nut (or washer)
protractor
string, 15 cm
tape

PREPARATION NOTES:

In this activity, the student constructs an astrolabe and uses it to measure the angles of stars above the horizon. You may wish to suggest that students and parents perform this activity together on a clear night.

PROCEDURE:

Part A: Constructing an Astrolabe

1. Tie one end of the string around the center of the straw.
2. Tie a nut or washer to the other end of the string.
3. Tape the protractor to the straw so that when the straw is held level, the string hangs at the 90° mark of the protractor.

Part B: Selecting Stars for Observation

1. Choose an observation site as far away from bright lights as possible. You will use this same observation site for all your observations. Locate north, south, east, and west directions.
2. For the north direction, locate the North Star. It is the last star in the handle of the Little Dipper.
3. Locate a bright star in each of the south, east, and west directions.

Part C: Star Positions

1. Decide on three times of the evening (each time one hour apart) for making your observations.
2. Locate the North Star. Using your astrolabe, sight the North Star along the top of the straw. Press and hold the string against the protractor when the star has been sighted. Read the number of degrees marked on the protractor by the string. Subtract the number of degrees from 90° to find the angle of the star from the horizon. Example: If the string has marked 60°, the star is 30° above the horizon (90° − 60° = 30°).
3. Record the time of the sighting and the angle of the star above the horizon.
4. Repeat Steps 2 and 3 for the stars you have selected in the south, east, and west.
5. One hour later, repeat your sightings and record the angles.
6. Once again, repeat your sightings one hour later.

OBSERVATIONS AND DATA:

Students answers will vary, but the stars should appear to move 15° each hour and should appear to move counterclockwise.

QUESTIONS AND CONCLUSIONS:

1. Based on your measured angles for each star, describe the apparent motion, if any, for each star.   *The stars appear to move in a westerly (counterclockwise) direction.*

2. (a) Do the stars appear to move in the same or different directions? *The stars seem to rotate around a central point—the North Star (Polaris).*
   (b) Does this seem to indicate that the stars are moving or that Earth is moving? Explain. *This observation could indicate that the stars are moving at a fixed rate around Earth, or Earth is rotating.*
3. What do your observations indicate about the direction of motion of Earth? *Because it is unlikely that all the stars are rotating at a fixed rate, one can decide that Earth is rotating from west to east (clockwise) with respect to the North Star.*

UNIT FIVE

Astronomy

chapter 21
Space Exploration

ACTIVITY 21-1: Action-Reaction (page 430)

OBJECTIVE: To observe action and reaction forces with an air-filled balloon.

CLASS TIME ALLOTMENT: 5 minutes.

MATERIALS:

rubber balloon

PREPARATION NOTES:

In this activity the student uses a toy balloon to demonstrate the action-reaction forces produced by an escaping gas. Extension: Vary the procedure by using a variety of balloons having different shapes and sizes. Have students compare results. Also, you can tape an inflated balloon to a soda straw. Draw a string through the straw to provide a line on which the balloon can travel when released.

PROCEDURE:

1. Blow up a balloon.
2. Quickly release the balloon.

OBSERVATIONS AND DATA:

The balloon flies away when the nozzle is opened.

QUESTIONS AND CONCLUSIONS:

The air trapped inside the balloon exerted an action force equally against the sides of the balloon. The balloon pushed back with a reaction force on the air inside the balloon. When the nozzle of the balloon was opened, the air trapped inside the balloon pushed against all surfaces except on the open nozzle. An unbalanced force on the side of the balloon opposite the nozzle resulted in thrust that propelled the balloon forward.

1. How is a rocket similar to a balloon? *The upward flight of a rocket is caused by an expanding gas (the action force) produced when a rocket burns fuel. The action force (thrust) builds up at the end of the chamber.*
2. Would the balloon move faster, slower, or at the same speed if the air pressure inside the room were reduced? *faster* Why? *The air friction on the outside surface of the balloon would be less.*
3. What is the force that moves the balloon called? *thrust*

ACTIVITY 21-2: Rocket Thrust (page 431)

OBJECTIVE: To demonstrate the operating principle of a rocket engine

CLASS TIME ALLOTMENT: 25 minutes.

MATERIALS:
baking soda—50 g
bottle—narrow-neck
cork
pencils—2 round
tissue—1 piece
vinegar—50 ml

PREPARATION NOTES:

In this activity the student demonstrates the operating principle of a rocket engine. The purpose for using the tissue is to retard the rate of reaction between the vinegar and the baking soda, ensuring a slow and even generation of carbon dioxide inside the bottle. Be certain students set the cork firmly in the mouth of the bottle, but not so tight that it will fail to pop out under the gas pressure.

PROCEDURE:
1. Pour the vinegar into the bottle.
2. Wrap the baking soda in the tissue. Place the tissue in the bottle into the vinegar.
3. Cork the bottle firmly. **CAUTION:** Do not cork too tight. Be certain the cork end of the bottle is not pointed toward any person.
4. Tip the corked bottle sideways and lay it on the pencils.

OBSERVATIONS AND DATA:

The vinegar and baking soda reacted vigorously in the bottle, producing a gas. Pressure increased in the bottle forcing the cork out. The bottle rolled backwards on the pencils.

QUESTIONS AND CONCLUSIONS:

A chemical reaction produces a gas that causes a thrust force inside the bottle. The gas in the activity is CO_2. The reaction is

$$[NaHCO_3 + CH_3COOH \longrightarrow CH_3COONa + CO_2 + H_2O]$$

[baking soda + vinegar $\longrightarrow$ sodium acetate + carbon dioxide + water]

1. How is the thrust force produced in the bottle? *The baking soda reacts with vinegar (acetic acid) to produce carbon dioxide gas. The gas pushes on all surfaces of the bottle and the cork, and the cork pushes back on the gas. The force of the gas on the cork creates an unbalanced force on the cork, and the cork is ejected from the bottle. An unbalanced force on the opposite end of the bottle from the nozzle, thrust, propels the bottle forward.*

2. Compare the action of the bottle to the action of a rocket. *The gases in the combustion chamber of a rocket have the same effect as that described on question 1. The thrust produced by a rocket must be greater than its weight for the rocket to lift off a launching pad.*

ACTIVITY 21-3: A Gyroscope (page 434)

OBJECTIVE: To observe the actions of a spinning gyroscope

CLASS TIME ALLOTMENT: 15 minutes.

MATERIALS: gyroscope
string—70 cm

PREPARATION NOTES:

In this activity the student investigates the principles of a spinning gyroscope. Review the concepts of force, inertia, and momentum and relate the ideas to a gyroscope.

PROCEDURE:

1. Start the gyroscope spinning.
2. Transfer the spinning gyroscope to the palm of your hand. Try to twist it in different directions.
3. Hold a string taut between your two hands. Have someone place the spinning gyroscope on the string.
4. Raise and lower your right (or left) hand (while the gyroscope is spinning on the strings) so it slides back and forth.

OBSERVATIONS AND DATA:

The spinning gyroscope always remained balanced in the hand and on the string.

QUESTIONS AND CONCLUSIONS:

A spinning gyroscope always maintains its balance.

1. What happens when you hold the gyroscope in your hand and try to twist it? *It stays the same.*
2. What did you observe when the gyroscope slid back and forth on the string? *The gyroscope slid up and down on the string while maintaining the original upright position.*
3. How does the speed at which the gyroscope turns affect its behavior? *The gyroscope is less stable at a slower speed.*

CHALLENGE: APPLYING SCIENTIFIC METHODS
The Force of Gravity

OBJECTIVE: To compare the falling rates of a steel ball and a glass marble

CLASS TIME ALLOTMENT: 20 minutes

MATERIALS:

glass marble
meter stick
rings stand and ring
steel ball (or heavy washer or nut)
watch or clock with second hand
string (or thread), 2 60-cm pieces
tape

PREPARATION NOTES:

In this activity students construct a simple pendulum and time its swing. Students then compare the falling times of a glass marble and a steel ball to determine if heavier objects fall faster than lighter objects. Caution students not to push the pendulum, but to simply release it. Pushing the pendulum will cause the timing of the ten swings to be incorrect, and results will be inaccurate.

PROCEDURE:

1. Tape one end of one string to the steel ball and one end of the other string to the glass marble.
2. Set up the equipment with the steel ball and string as shown below.

FIGURE 21-1

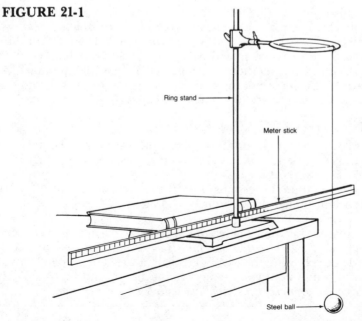

Ring stand

Meter stick

Steel ball

3. Pull the ball back 15 cm and release it. Use a clock or watch with second hand to determine the number of seconds it takes for 10 complete swings. NOTE: In a complete swing, the ball swings from A to B and back to A. Record the number of seconds required for 10 complete swings.

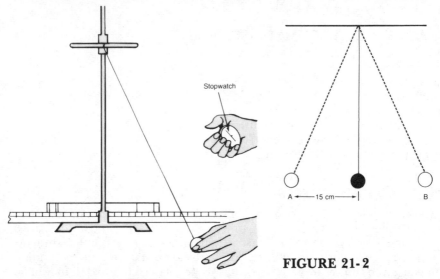

FIGURE 21-2

4. Now pull the steel ball back 30 cm and determine the number of seconds it takes for 10 complete swings. Record the number of seconds.
5. Attach the string with the marble near the string with the steel ball. Make sure that the string with the marble is exactly the same length as the string with the steel ball. Then remove the string with the steel ball.
6. Using the marble, repeat Steps 3 and 4. Record the number of seconds for each trial.

OBSERVATIONS AND DATA:

Student results will vary. The following data is for a string length of 55.0 cm. When pulled back 15 cm, the steel ball took 15.0 s to complete 10 swings. The steel ball took 15.2 s to complete 10 swings when pulled back 30 cm. The glass marble took 15.2 s when pulled back both 15 and 30 cm. The time required for 10 swings of a pendulum can be calculated by the equation $T = 2\pi\sqrt{l/g}$, where 1 is the length of the string to the center of the ball and g is the acceleration due to gravity (980 cm/s² at sea-level).

QUESTIONS AND CONCLUSIONS:

1. (a) What was the time (in seconds for 10 complete swings of the steel ball when pulled back 15 cm?   *Answers will vary.*
   (b) 30 cm?   *Answers will vary.*
2. (a) What was the time (in seconds) for 10 complete swings of the glass marble when pulled back 15 cm?   *Answers will vary.*
   (b) 30 cm? Answers will vary.
3. In one complete swing, how many times was the steel ball or glass marble actually falling?   *Twice—The ball falls from A to B and from B to A*
4. If you dropped a bowling ball and glass ball at the same time off a tall building, which one would you expect to hit the ground first?   *They should both hit the ground at the same time (neglecting air friction).*

UNIT SIX

Human Ecology

chapter 22
People and Resources

ACTIVITY 22-1: The Difference One Child Makes (page 456)

OBJECTIVE: To analyze the effect that an increase of one child per family can have on the overall population growth.

CLASS TIME ALLOTMENT: 15 minutes.

MATERIALS: Figure 22-1, p. 456

PREPARATION NOTES:

In this activity the student analyzes the effect that an average of one child per family increase can have on the overall population growth. An average of three children per family causes an exponential (geometric) increase in population growth. At a rate of two children per family the number of new children born would eventually equal the replacement rate and population growth would level off. The rate of growth of a country's population depends on the birth rate, death rate, immigration, and emigration.

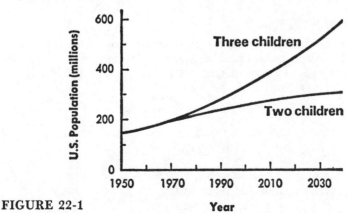

FIGURE 22-1

PROCEDURE:
1. Study the graph
2. Determine how the diffence of one child per family will affect the size of the United States population in 2010, and in 2030.

OBSERVATIONS AND DATA:
The lines on the graph indicate a small population increase with two children per family and a very rapid population increase with three children per family.

QUESTIONS AND CONCLUSIONS:
One extra child per family has a great effect on the population.
1. How will a difference of one child per family affect the size of the United States population in the year 2010?   *It will cause an increase of 100 million.* 2030?   *250 million increase*
2. What affect would this difference have on the food needs those years?   *The food needs would be so much greater that it would be difficult to provide adequate food supplies.*
3. Is it possible to increase food production to provide for an increase in population?   *Food production can be increased. However, many people are already starving to death. It is doubtful that food production can ever keep up with population increase.*

ACTIVITY 22-2: Resources (page 458)

OBJECTIVE: To develop an understanding of renewable and nonrenewable resources

CLASS TIME ALLOTMENT: 20 minutes.

MATERIALS:
cardboard—two large pieces
glue
marking pen
old magazines
scissors

PREPARATION NOTES:
In this activity the student will develop an understanding of renewable and nonrenewable resources by making picture displays of each type of resource. You may wish to assign this activity for homework and have each student bring in one picture.

PROCEDURE:
1. Cut pictures of renewable resources from old magazines.
2. Glue them to a large piece of cardboard.
3. Label each resource.
4. Explain why each one is considered a renewable resource.
5. Do the same for nonrenewable resources.

OBSERVATIONS AND DATA:

Examples of renewable resources are garden plants, forests, fish stocks, and wildlife species. An example of a nonrenewable resource is coal. Iron, copper, sulfur, and other minerals can be partially recovered by recycling.

QUESTIONS AND CONCLUSIONS:

Renewable resources are those that can be replaced within a person's lifetime. After a crop of lettuce is eaten, more can be planted and harvested. Wildlife becomes a nonrenewable resource if it becomes extinct. A nonrenewable resource, such as coal or oil, cannot be replaced once the deposits are gone.

1. How is each renewable resource renewed?   *Answers will vary depending on the resource.*

ACTIVITY 22-3: Food Price Comparison (page 460)

OBJECTIVE: To compare the costs of foods and hypothesize reasons for differences in the costs of different kinds of foods

CLASS TIME ALLOTMENT: 20 minutes.

MATERIALS:

newspaper—full page shopping advertisement

PREPARATION NOTES:

In this activity the student compares the costs of goods and hypothesizes reasons for differences in the costs of different kinds of foods. The relative value of food may be considered a function of their protein content, their sources and availability, and the amount of processing involved in their marketing.

PROCEDURE:

1. Obtain a full-page newspaper advertisement for a local supermarket.
2. Compare the prices of fruits and vegetables with the prices of fish and meat.
3. Compare the prices of bread and packaged cereals.

OBSERVATIONS AND DATA:

The prices of meat and fish per unit weight are usually higher than fruits or vegetables. The prices of packaged cereals are higher than the price of bread products.

QUESTIONS AND CONCLUSIONS:

Prices are higher for foods that require packaging, extensive processing, and are very perishable.

1. How many factors can you name that affect the price of food?   *Factors that affect the price of food include nutritional value, supply and demand, season of the year, amount of processing that has gone into making the product, and perishability.*
2. Which factor do you think is the most important?   *Answers will vary.*

ADDITIONAL QUESTIONS:

3. How could the season affect the price of some foods? *Some foods are not available in certain areas during certain seasons and must be transported. Transportation costs increase the price of food.*

ADDITIONAL ACTIVITY: Types of Foods Eaten (section 22:3)

OBJECTIVE: To show a variety of foods we eat and their different sources

CLASS TIME ALLOTMENT: 20 minutes.

MATERIALS:
paper
pencil

PREPARATION NOTES:

In this activity the student categorizes different types of foods eaten in one day into source groups.

PROCEDURE:

1. Using the data table below, list all the foods you ate yesterday under "Foods Eaten".
2. Determine if each food came from a grain, fruit, green vegetable, or an animal, and place a mark in the appropriate column.
3. Compile class data on the chalkboard.

OBSERVATIONS AND DATA:

FOODS EATEN	GRAINS (WHEAT, RICE, CORN)	FRUITS	GREEN VEGETABLES	ANIMALS

Students' lists will be somewhat different, but each student will probably have eaten foods from more than one group.

QUESTIONS AND CONCLUSIONS:

Foods that we eat come from various sources.

1. What food item was eaten most? *Answers will vary.*
2. What food item was eaten least? *Answers will vary.*
3. What are some things that influence the kinds of food people eat? *preference, cost, religion, environment, culture, etc.*

ADDITIONAL ACTIVITY: Variety of Foods (section 22:3)

OBJECTIVE: To illustrate the many different types of food and their sources

CLASS TIME ALLOTMENT: 10 minutes each day for a week, 20 minutes final day.

MATERIALS:
paper
pencil

PREPARATION NOTES:
In this activity the student categorizes different types of foods into source eating locations. NOTE: The school cafeteria list should be compiled over a five-day period. This makes the list more reasonable to compare against the offerings of a restaurant.

PROCEDURE:
1. Make a list of foods served in the school cafeteria over a five-day period.
2. Make a list of foods served at a local fast-food restaurant.
3. Compare the two lists to see how they are alike and different.

OBSERVATIONS AND DATA:
The cafeteria will probably have a larger variety of foods than the fast-food restaurant. Both the cafeteria and fast-food restaurant have foods from plants and animals.

QUESTIONS AND CONCLUSIONS:
1. How are the two lists alike?   *Some foods are served at both locations. Answers will vary as to which foods are similar.*
2. How are the two lists different?   *Some foods are not served at both locations. Answers will vary as to which foods are different.*
3. Which list has the most variety?   *Answers may vary, but usually the cafeteria list will show more variety.*
4. Which foods from the two lists are from plants?   *will vary*
5. Which foods from the two lists are from animals?   *will vary*

ADDITIONAL ACTIVITY: Water Holding Capacity of Soil (Section 22:4)

OBJECTIVE: To demonstrate that various types of soils hold different amounts of water

CLASS TIME ALLOTMENT: 15 minutes

MATERIALS:
graduated cylinder   sand—dry
paper cups—3   topsoil—dry
paper towels   water
potting soil

PREPARATION NOTES:

In this activity the student will experimentally determine the water holding capacity of three types of soils.

PROCEDURE:

1. Punch small holes in the bottoms of three paper cups.
2. Fill one cup three-fourths full of dry topsoil.
3. Fill the second cup three-fourths full of dry sand.
4. Fill the third cup three-fourths full of dry potting soil rich in humus.
5. Place the cups on a piece of paper towel.
6. Fill a graduated cylinder with water and record the amount of water in mL in column A of the chart.
7. Slowly pour water from the cylinder in the cup of topsoil. Pour the water slowly enough so that no water stands on the surface of the soil.
8. Pour water until it begins to run out of the holes in the bottom of a cup.
9. Record the amount of water left in the cylinder in column B of the chart.
10. Calculate the amount of water held by the topsoil and record it in column C. (Subtract B from A)
11. Repeat this procedure (Steps 6-10) with each of the other two cups.

OBSERVATIONS AND DATA:

	A	B	C
SOIL TYPE	AMOUNT OF WATER IN CYLINDER AT START	AMOUNT OF WATER IN CYLINDER AT FINISH	AMOUNT OF WATER HELD IN SOIL
Topsoil			
Sand			
Potting soil			

The potting soil held most of the water; the topsoil held less water than the potting soil; and the sand held the least water.

QUESTIONS AND CONCLUSIONS:

1. Why is there a difference in the water holding capacity of the soils?   *different amounts of humus; the more humus in the soil, the more water the soil can hold*
2. How might soil differences affect irrigation?   *Soil rich in humus will hold more water and will need less irrigation than a soil with less humus.*
3. How well would a soil rich in clay hold water?   *not very well* Why?   *Clay particles are so tighly packed together that little water can be absorbed.*

ACTIVITY 22-4: Loss of Water by Evaporation (page 463)

OBJECTIVE: To compare the rate of evaporation of water under different conditions

CLASS TIME ALLOTMENT: 10 minutes each day for several days.

MATERIALS:

beaker—3, 25 ml
cotton cloth—10 cm × 10 cm
graduated cylinder—10 ml
water

PREPARATION NOTES:

In this activity the student compares the rate of evaporation of water under different conditions. Relate this observation to drip irrigation in which the loss of irrigated water is significantly reduced through the use of a system in which the water is enclosed in pipes or tubes.

PROCEDURE:

1. Add 10 mL of water to each of three small beakers.
2. Place two beakers on a small windowsill where they will be in the sun.
3. Cover one of these two beakers with a piece of cotton cloth.
4. Place the third beaker in the shade.
5. Observe the three beakers each day until all the water has evaporated from one of them.

OBSERVATIONS AND DATA:

The uncovered beaker on the windowsill in the sun lost its water the fastest. The uncovered beaker in the shade had lost some water, but not all. The covered beaker had the most water left in it.

QUESTIONS AND CONCLUSIONS:

Water evaporates more quickly when it is uncovered and exposed to warmth.
1. Why is evaporation slower in the covered beaker in the sun and uncovered beaker in the shade?   *covering and lowering the water's temperature slow evaporation*
2. What is evaporation?   *loss of water to the atmosphere*
3. In what types of areas would evaporation be the greatest?   *where the soil is uncovered and the temperature very warm, such as a desert*
4. How can loss of water by evaporation be slowed down in irrigation?   *covering the soil or irrigation pipes instead of open trenches and using a drip irrigation process*

ACTIVITY 22-5: Mineral Resources (page 466)

OBJECTIVE: To increase the student's understanding of the extensive use of minerals in producing things that people use daily

CLASS TIME ALLOTMENT: 10 minutes.

MATERIALS:

paper
pencil

PREPARATION NOTES:

In this activity the student identifies objects in his/her surroundings that are made from minerals. The purpose of the activity is to increase the student's understanding of the extensive use of minerals in producing things that people use daily.

PROCEDURE:

1. Look around your classroom.
2. List 15 different objects you see.

OBSERVATIONS AND DATA:

Lists of different objects will vary. There will probably be more objects from mineral resources than from living resources.

QUESTIONS AND CONCLUSIONS:

1. How many objects on your list are made from mineral resources?   *will vary—examples: plaster, steel, chalk, blackboard, windows*
2. How many are made from living resources?   *will vary—examples: leather, wood, cotton, wool, plastic, paper*

ADDITIONAL ACTIVITY: Efficient Burning of Gas
(section 22:7)

OBJECTIVE: To demonstrate the efficiency of a gas flame depends upon the air-gas mixture and can be detected by a flame color

CLASS TIME ALLOTMENT: 10 minutes.

MATERIALS:

glass plate—small
laboratory burner
metal tongs
safety goggles

PREPARATION NOTES:

In this activity the student learns the basic concepts of gas flames, including efficiency of burning. Color is the diagnostic characteristic of flame efficiency.

PROCEDURE:

1. Obtain a laboratory burner and connect it to a gas outlet. Put on your safety goggles.
2. Turn on the gas and light the burner.
3. Adjust the height of the flame with the valve at the bottom.
4. Adjust the color of the flame with the collar.
5. Change the flame from blue to yellow.
6. Hold a small glass plate in the yellow flame with the metal tongs.
7. Record your observations.
8. Adjust the flame back to blue.
9. Find the tip of the inner cone inside the blue flame. This point has the highest temperature. **CAUTION:** Do not put the glass plate in the blue flame. The high temperature will shatter the glass.

OBSERVATIONS AND DATA:

When the collar was adjusted to allow more air in the gas, the flame color was yellow. The yellow flame was much more irregular-shaped than the blue flame. When the glass plate was put in the yellow flame, moisture probably appeared briefly on the plate. The plate became covered with black soot (carbon particles).

QUESTIONS AND CONCLUSIONS:

A yellow flame is not efficient because it leaves unburned soot. A inefficient flame results from too much air mixed with the gas. A blue flame is an efficient flame. It has a good air-gas mixture and is burning more complete.

1. From where did the water and soot that formed on the glass come? *the gas (products of incomplete burning)*
2. Which is hotter, the blue flame or the yellow flame? *blue flame* Why? *There is a better mixture of gas and air that results in a more efficient flame and more complete carbon burning. Since the burning is more complete, the flame is hotter.*
3. Why is the yellow flame not efficient? *because it leaves unburned soot (carbon particles)*
4. Why does a burner with a yellow flame waste energy? *Not all of the gas is being burned.*
5. If you have a furnace in your home, why should you have the gas flame checked? *to see if it is burning efficiently and not wasting energy*

ADDITIONAL ACTIVITY: Destructive Distillation of Wood (section 22:7)

OBJECTIVE: To illustrate that when wood splints are heated a flammable gas is produced

CLASS TIME ALLOTMENT: 20 minutes.

MATERIALS:

glass bottle	ring stand with test tube clamp
glass tubing	rubber stopper to fit test
laboratory burner	tube—one hole
matches	rubber stopper to fit glass
mineral oil or water	bottle—two hole
Pyrex test tube	wooden splints—6

PREPARATION NOTES:

This activity should be performed as a demonstration. The materials and method are an example of the simple distillation technique. You may wish to expand on this idea and discuss fractional distillation of petroleum into various components.

PROCEDURE:

1. Break up six wooden splints into small pieces, and then place them into a Pyrex test tube.
2. Clamp the test tube to a ring stand so its mouth tips down slightly.

3. Using the one-hole rubber stopper, connect the test tube to a glass delivery tube. The other end of the delivery tube should connect to the two-hole rubber stopper in a glass bottle.
4. Extend the delivery tube well down into the bottle.
5. Insert a piece of glass tubing with a tip drawn into a jet in the other hole. **CAUTION:** It is best to connect the delivery tube and jet tube to the rubber stoppers first. Use water or mineral oil to lubricate the glass tubing before you push it through the stoppers. Then insert the test tube and glass bottle.
6. Heat the test tube strongly with a laboratory burner.
7. Ignite the gas that comes out of the jet with a lighted match. NOTE: If the jet flame goes out, it is due to the presence of water vapor in the fuel gas.

OBSERVATIONS AND DATA:

The wood splints turned dark in color when heated. As they were heated, a gas came out of the jet and could be ignited.

QUESTIONS AND CONCLUSIONS:

A flammable gas is produced when wood splints are heated.
1. What causes the jet flame to sometimes go out?   *Water vapor is sometimes produced, and puts out the flame.*
2. How could the amount of water vapor have been reduced?   *drying the wood splints before heating*
3. What is the black substance left in the test tube after heating?   *carbon*
4. How is coal related to wood?   *Coal is formed from plant materials.*
5. Could coal have served as the fuel in the activity instead of the wood splints?   *yes* Why?   *Coal contains the same energy from plants as the wood splints.*
6. Which would have produced a jet flame the longest?   *coal* Why?   *Coal is much more concentrated plant material and contains more energy.*

CHALLENGE: APPLYING SCIENTIFIC METHODS
Food energy

OBJECTIVE: To construct a calorimeter to determine how much energy is in food

CLASS TIME ALLOTMENT: One period.

MATERIALS:

balance	sugar cubes, 2	rubber stopper, 1-hole
beaker, 100 mL	goggles	thermometer, Celcius
beaker tongs	graduated cylinder	water
buret clamp	matches, long stemmed	wire gauze, 2
evaporating dish	ring stand and ring	

PREPARATION NOTES:

In this activity students construct a simple calorimeter to determine how much energy is in food. Caution students to wear goggles when using matches and burning food. Beaker tongs should be used to move the beaker during and after burning the food. Students should moisten the tip of the thermometer with glycerin or water before inserting in the stopper and should wrap their hands in cloth toweling and gently twist the thermometer into the stopper hole. When heating, avoid having thermometer in contact with the bottom or side of the beaker.

PROCEDURE:

1. Cover the evaporating dish with a wire gauze and place on the base of the ring stand. Put a sugar cube on top of the wire gauze. Position the ring 2 cm above the sugar cube. Place a second piece of wire gauze on the ring, and position the beaker on the ring/gauze assembly. Insert the thermometer into the one-hole stopper. **CAUTION:** Moisten the tip of the thermometer with glycerin or water before inserting in the stopper. Wrap your hands in cloth toweling and gently twist the thermometer into the stopper hole. Place the stopper in the buret clamp. Attach the clamp to the ring stand so that the thermometer is in the beaker. **CAUTION:** Position the thermometer so that it does not touch the bottom or sides of the beaker.
2. Measure the mass of the sugar cube and record.
3. Add exactly 20 mL of water to the beaker. Record the volume and the mass of the water. NOTE: One milliliter of water has a mass of one gram.
4. Measure the temperature of the water and record as Beginning Water Temperature.
5. Raise the thermometer and remove the beaker from the ring.
6. Light the food sample with the match. **CAUTION:** Wear goggles when working with matches.
7. Place the beaker on the ring directly over the burning food sample. **CAUTION:** Use beaker tongs to move the beaker over the flame. Lower the thermometer into the water. Avoid contact between the thermometer and the beaker.
8. If complete burning does not occur, relight the sample.
9. When burning is complete, measure the temperature of the water and record as Final Water Temperature.
10. Repeat Steps 2 through 9 for a second trial. Replace the water in the beaker with water at near room temperature before beginning Trial 2. **CAUTION:** Beaker may be hot. Use breaker tongs to move beaker.
11. Calculate the temperature change of the water for both trials and record. NOTE: Temperature change = Final water temperature − Beginning water temperature.
12. Calculate the heat absorbed by the water for each trial by using the following equation. Heat absorbed + Mass of water × Temperature change of water × 4.18 J/g.C°.
13. Record the heat absorbed.
14. Calculate the average heat absorbed [(Trial 1 + Trial 2)/2].

OBSERVATIONS AND DATA:

Student data will vary, however, the temperature change of the water should be close to 55°C. The heat absorbed by the water should average 4550 J.

QUESTIONS AND CONCLUSIONS:

1. When 1 g of sugar is burned, about 5400 J of energy are released. Compare this amount of energy with your calculations.   *Student answers will vary. The average value of heat absorbed will be less than the given value even though more than 1 g of sugar was burned.*

2. In this experiment, does the water absorb all the heat released by the burning food? Explain.   *No, heat is lost to the environment and to other parts of the calorimeter.*

---

chapter 23

People and Their Environment

ACTIVITY 23-1: Acid Water (page 484)

OBJECTIVE: To show that the gas produced by a burning candle turns water to acid

CLASS TIME ALLOTMENT: 25 minutes.

MATERIALS:

bromothymol blue
candle
dropper
glass jar
glass plate—15 cm × 15 cm
graduated cylinder—10 mL
matches
test tube
water—5 mL

PREPARATION NOTES:

In this activity the student uses bromothymol blue to show that the gas produced by a burning candle turns water acidic. Carbon dioxide produced by the burning candle dissolves in the water and forms a weak solution of carbonic acid.

PROCEDURE:

1. Add drops of bromothymol blue to 5 mL of water in a test tube until the water becomes light blue.
2. Set a small candle in a glass jar. Light the candle and place a glass plate over the jar.
3. After the candle goes out, add the bromothymol blue solution in the test tube to the jar. Replace the glass cover and shake the jar vigorously.
4. Observe what happens.

OBSERVATIONS AND DATA:

Students should observe that the water turns yellow.

QUESTIONS AND CONCLUSIONS:

Nitrogen oxides and sulfur oxides produce acid rain.

1. What gas caused the water to turn acidic?   *carbon dioxide*
2. Name two other gases that make water acidic when they dissolve?   *Nitrogen oxides, sulfur oxides*

ACTIVITY 23-2: Decay and Oxygen (page 486)

OBJECTIVE: To use an indicator to show that decay of vegetation turns water acidic

CLASS TIME ALLOTMENT: 20 minutes.

MATERIALS:

bromothymol blue
dried grass
dropper
jars with screw caps—2 small

PREPARATION NOTES:

In this activity the student uses bromothymol blue as an indicator to show that decay of vegetation turns water acidic. The production of acid causes a decrease in the dissolved oxygen content of the water. The decreased content endangers the lives of water organisms. Encourage students to do research and prepare reports about Lake Erie, the Hudson River, or other polluted water bodies, in relation to this activity.

PROCEDURE:

1. Obtain two small jars with caps that screw on tight. Fill each jar half full of water. Add drops of bromothymol blue to each jar until the water turns light blue.
2. Add some dried grass to one jar.
3. Completely fill each jar with water and screw the caps on tight. Make certain the jars are completely full of water, and that there is no air in the tops.
4. Let the jars stand for five days.
5. Observe the jars each day and record any changes you see.

OBSERVATIONS AND DATA:

A change in color of the blue indicator shows that oxygen is being used. A color change occurs only in the jar with dried grass.

QUESTIONS AND CONCLUSIONS:

As material decays in water, it consumes oxygen and removes dissolved oxygen from the water.

1. How does decay change the oxygen content of the water?   *It decreases the oxygen content.*
2. What does the color change in the jar with the dried grass indicate?   *that the water becomes acidic*
3. Which jar is the control?   *the jar with only water and bromothymol blue*

ACTIVITY 23-3: Analysis of Trash (page 494)

OBJECTIVE: To compare the kinds of solid waste disposed of at school and at home

CLASS TIME ALLOTMENT: 15 minutes.

MATERIALS:

paper
pencil

PREPARATION NOTES:

In this activity the student compares the kinds of solid waste disposed of at school and at home. It is recommended that students work in pairs: one student noting the kinds of trash thrown away, and the other student writing down the data as it is noted. Suggest that students develop a tally sheet before doing this activity.

PROCEDURE:

1. Obtain permission to observe the disposal of trash into a cafeteria trash container.
2. Stand by the trash container and observe the objects students throw away.
3. Keep a record of the number of objects that are (a) paper, (b) metal, (c) plastic, and (d) food. Organize that data in a table. When you have counted 100 objects, total the number in each group.
4. Repeat this procedure by keeping track of objects thrown away into a home trash container during a single day.
5. Calculate the percent of objects for each group.

OBSERVATIONS AND DATA:

Data will vary.

WHERE	PAPER	METAL	PLASTIC	FOOD
Cafeteria				
Home				

QUESTIONS AND CONCLUSIONS:

1. How are the contents of two trash containers alike and different?   *The school trash container will hold mostly food, paper, and plastic. The home trash container will hold waste from the home and family members.*

CHALLENGE: APPLYING SCIENTIFIC METHODS
Thermal Pollution

OBJECTIVE: To determine how water temperature affects organisms

CLASS TIME ALLOTMENT: One period.

MATERIALS:

baby food jar with lid
beakers, 100mL, 2
burner
burner stand

dip net
glass marking pencil
goggles
goldfish

graduated cylinder
thermometer, Celsius
watch with second hand

PREPARATION NOTES:

In this activity students determine the effect of increased temperature on the activity level of a goldfish. The mosquito fish (Gambusia) may be used in place of a goldfish. Caution students that glassware must be clean before the fish is placed in it. Dirty glassware can cause the death of the fish. Also caution students to wear goggles while heating the water. Note that in a natural environment, water temperature changes gradually. Because the body temperature of a fish adapts to its environment, fish usually have time to adapt or move when water temperature changes.

PROCEDURE:

1. Measure 30 mL water into each of the two beakers. Label one beaker A and the other B.
2. Fill the baby food jar with water from the fish tank. Using the dip net, move the fish from the tank to the baby food jar. Put on the lid and place the baby food jar in beaker A.
3. Wait three minutes and then measure the temperature of the water in beaker A and record.
4. Determine the activity level (breathing rate) of the fish by counting the number of times the fish opens and closes its mouth in 20 seconds. Record this number.
5. Repeat Step 4 two more times and record your results. NOTE: If the goldfish moves about and interrupts your counting, start over.
6. Record any other observations about the activity of the fish.
7. Calculate the average [(Trial 1 + Trial 2 + Trial 3)/3] and record.
8. Remove the baby food jar from beaker A. Remove the lid and allow the jar to sit for three minutes. Then carefully put the fish back into the fish tank. Empty the contents of the baby food jar.
9. Place beaker B on the burner stand and heat until the water temperature is 35°C.
10. Carefully remove the beaker from the stand.
11. Fill the baby food jar with water from the fish tank. Place the fish in the baby food jar using the dip net. Put on the lid and place the jar in beaker B.
12. Wait three minutes and then determine the activity level of the fish as you did in Step 4. Record your results.
13. Repeat the 20 second counting two more times and record. Calculate and record the average.
14. Remove the baby food jar from beaker B. Remove the lid and allow the jar to sit for three minutes. Then carefully put the fish back into the tank.

OBSERVATIONS AND DATA:

Results will vary, however, students should observe a higher breathing rate when the fish is in beaker B.

QUESTIONS AND CONCLUSIONS:

1. What was the average breathing rate of the goldfish when it was in beaker A?   *Results will vary.*
2. What was the average breathing rate of the goldfish when it was in beaker B?   *Results will vary, however, the answer should be higher than for Question 1.*
3. What was the effect of increased water temperature on the breathing rate of the fish.   *The breathing rate increased.*
4. Did the fish seem more active in the warmer or the cooler water?   *The fish was more active in the warmer water.*
5. Would a fish breathe faster or slower in an environment low in oxygen? Explain.   *A fish would breathe faster in order to get a sufficient amount of oxygen.*
6. How do you think increasing the water temperature affects the amount of oxygen in the water?   *The solubility of a gas in a liquid decreases with increasing temperature of the liquid.*
7. A fish is a cold-blooded animal (exothermic). Its body temperature changes gradually as the water temperature changes. If a sudden change in the temperature occurs, the fish must move or die. What would happen to the fish population in a lake where hot steam was pumped in.
   (a) once?   *The fish might be killed or leave and then return.*
   (b) once a day?   *The fish would probably leave the area or be killed.*

REFERENCE TABLES

OXIDATION NUMBERS OF COMMON MONATOMIC IONS

1 +	2 +	3 +	4 +
cesium, Cs^+ copper (I), Cu^+ hydrogen, H^+ lithium, Li^+ potassium, K^+ rubidium, Rb^+ silver, Ag^+ sodium, Na^+ thallium (I), Tl^+	barium, Ba^{2+} cadmium, Cd^{2+} calcium, Ca^{2+} cobalt (II), Co^{2+} copper (II), Cu^{2+} iron (II), Fe^{2+} lead (II), Pb^{2+} magnesium, Mg^{2+} manganese (II), Mn^{2+} mercury (II), Hg^{2+} nickel (II), Ni^{2+} strontium, Sr^{2+} tin (II), Sn^{2+} zinc, Zn^{2+}	aluminum, Al^{3+} bismuth (III), Bi^{3+} cerium (III), Ce^{3+} chromium (III), Cr^{3+} gallium (III), Ga^{3+} iron (III), Fe^{3+}	germanium (IV), Ge^{4+} lead (IV), Pb^{4+} silicon (IV), Si^{4+} thorium (IV), Th^{4+} tin (IV), Sn^{4+} zirconium (IV), Zr^{4+}
1 −	2 −	3 −	4 −
bromide, Br^- chloride, Cl^- fluoride, F^- hydride, H^- iodide, I^-	oxide, O^{2-} selenide, Se^{2-} sulfide, S^{2-} telluride, Te^{2-}	nitride, N^{3-} phosphide, P^{3-}	carbide, C^{4-}

CHARGES OF COMMON POLYATOMIC IONS

1+		
ammonium, NH_4^+		
1 −	2 −	3 −
acetate, $C_2H_3O_2^-$ chlorate, ClO_3^- cyanide, CN^- hydroxide, OH^- hypochlorite, ClO^- iodate, IO_3^- nitrate, NO_3^- nitrite, NO_2^- perchlorate, ClO_4^-	carbonate, CO_3^{2-} hexafluorosilicate, SiF_6^{2-} oxalate, $C_2O_4^{2-}$ selenate, SeO_4^{2-} silicate, SiO_3^{2-} sulfate, SO_4^{2-} tartrate, $C_4H_4O_6^{2-}$	arsenate, AsO_4^{3-} phosphate, PO_4^{3-}

SOLUBILITY OF COMMON COMPOUNDS IN WATER

Common compounds which contain the following ions are soluble.
1. sodium (Na^+), potassium (K^+), ammonium (NH_4^+)
2. nitrates (NO_3^-)
3. acetates ($C_2H_3O_2^-$), except silver acetate, which is only moderately soluble
4. chlorides (Cl^-), except silver, mercury (I), and lead chlorides, $PbCl_2$ is soluble in hot water
5. sulfates (SO_4^{2-}), except barium and lead sulfates. Calcium, mercury (I), and silver sulfates are slightly soluble.

Common compounds which contain the following ions are insoluble.
1. silver, (Ag^+), except silver nitrate and silver perchlorate
2. sulfides (S^{2-}), except those of sodium, potassium, ammonium, magnesium, barium, and calcium
3. carbonates (CO_3^{2-}), except those of sodium, potassium, and ammonium
4. phosphates (PO_4^{3-}), except those of sodium, potassium, and ammonium hydroxides (OH^-), except those of sodium, potassium, ammonium, and barium

The Periodic Table
(Based on Carbon 12 = 12.0000)

Key: Atomic number / Element symbol / Average atomic mass

Example: 12 / Mg / Magnesium / 24.305

IA	IIA	IIIB	IVB	VB	VIB	VIIB	VIIIB	VIIIB	VIIIB	IB	IIB	IIIA	IVA	VA	VIA	VIIA	VIIIA
1 H Hydrogen 1.0079																	2 He Helium 4.00260
3 Li Lithium 6.941	4 Be Beryllium 9.01218											5 B Boron 10.82	6 C Carbon 12.011	7 N Nitrogen 14.0067	8 O Oxygen 15.9994	9 F Fluorine 18.998403	10 Ne Neon 20.179
11 Na Sodium 22.9898	12 Mg Magnesium 24.305											13 Al Aluminum 26.98154	14 Si Silicon 28.0855	15 P Phosphorus 30.97376	16 S Sulfur 32.06	17 Cl Chlorine 35.453	18 Ar Argon 39.948
19 K Potassium 39.0983	20 Ca Calcium 40.08	21 Sc Scandium 44.9559	22 Ti Titanium 47.90	23 V Vanadium 50.9414	24 Cr Chromium 51.996	25 Mn Manganese 54.9380	26 Fe Iron 55.847	27 Co Cobalt 58.9332	28 Ni Nickel 58.70	29 Cu Copper 63.546	30 Zn Zinc 65.38	31 Ga Gallium 69.72	32 Ge Germanium 72.59	33 As Arsenic 74.9216	34 Se Selenium 78.96	35 Br Bromine 79.904	36 Kr Krypton 83.80
37 Rb Rubidium 85.4678	38 Sr Strontium 87.62	39 Y Yttrium 88.9059	40 Zr Zirconium 91.22	41 Nb Niobium 92.9064	42 Mo Molybdenum 95.94	43 Tc Technetium 96.9062	44 Ru Ruthenium 101.07	45 Rh Rhodium 102.9055	46 Pd Palladium 106.4	47 Ag Silver 107.868	48 Cd Cadmium 112.41	49 In Indium 114.82	50 Sn Tin 118.69	51 Sb Antimony 121.75	52 Te Tellurium 127.60	53 I Iodine 126.9045	54 Xe Xenon 131.30
55 Cs Cesium 132.9054	56 Ba Barium 137.34	71 Lu Lutetium 174.97	72 Hf Hafnium 178.49	73 Ta Tantalum 180.9479	74 W Tungsten 183.85	75 Re Rhenium 186.207	76 Os Osmium 190.2	77 Ir Iridium 192.22	78 Pt Platinum 195.09	79 Au Gold 196.9665	80 Hg Mercury 200.59	81 Tl Thallium 204.37	82 Pb Lead 207.2	83 Bi Bismuth 208.9804	84 Po Polonium 208.9824	85 At Astatine 209.9870	86 Rn Radon 222
87 Fr Francium 223.0197	88 Ra Radium 226	103 Lr Lawrencium 256.999	104* 257	105* 260	106* 263	107* 258	108* 265	109* 266									

Transition Metals

Rare Earth Elements

LANTHANIDE SERIES:

57 La Lanthanum 138.9055	58 Ce Cerium 140.12	59 Pr Praseodymium 140.9077	60 Nd Neodymium 144.24	61 Pm Promethium 144.9179	62 Sm Samarium 150.4	63 Eu Europium 151.96	64 Gd Gadolinium 157.25	65 Tb Terbium 158.9254	66 Dy Dysprosium 162.50	67 Ho Holmium 164.9304	68 Er Erbium 167.26	69 Tm Thulium 168.9342	70 Yb Ytterbium 173.04

ACTINIDE SERIES:

89 Ac Actinium 227.0274	90 Th Thorium 232.0381	91 Pa Protactinium 231.0359	92 U Uranium 238.029	93 Np Neptunium 237.0482	94 Pu Plutonium 244.0642	95 Am Americium 243.0614	96 Cm Curium 247.0703	97 Bk Berkelium 247.0703	98 Cf Californium 251.0796	99 Es Einsteinium 254.0880	100 Fm Fermium 257.0951	101 Md Mendelevium 258.0986	102 No Nobelium 259.1009

*Names for elements 104 through 109 have not been approved by the IUPAC.